the Ultimate Guide to beauty

anjana gosai

Author Anjana Gosai

First published in 2008 by Glentree Publishing Limited
20 A Hilton Crescent, West Bridgford, Nottingham, NG2 6HT, UK
www.glentree.eu
Copyright © Glentree Publishing Limited and Anjana Gosai

Text, photography and illustration copyright ©
Anjana Gosai

All picture credits given on page 204

ISBN : 978-1-905581-25-2

Printed and bound by New Model Impex (P) Ltd. (India)

CONTENTS

INTRODUCTION

This book is the culmination of years of work, research and plenty of fun along the way.

My love affair with beauty began as a young girl attracted to the magical world of my mothers dressing table. Amongst the lipsticks and mascaras my fascination blossomed.

At the age of 19, I finished university. I had always felt that my destiny lay somewhere between the vast world of beauty and the women's magazines I purchased religiously.

My first foray into this industry came when I started modelling. Through the endless photo shoots and fashion shows, I soon gained a respect for the profession when I realized the necessity of keeping one's self in peak condition.

When an opportunity came up to work at Asian Woman, a leading women's magazine in the UK, as a beauty journalist, I grabbed it with both hands. I knew that this job would rest perfectly with my work and open the door to the industry I admired.

Through modelling I had already learnt so much about beauty from a first hand point of view, but now as a beauty journalist I had a unique opportunity to take my interest further. I am now living my dream. I'm lucky enough to be invited to try countless treatments, and am sent sacks full of beauty goodies, which I enjoy reviewing.

Increasingly, more readers of all ages are writing to me and asking me for advice. Friends and strangers alike, regularly question me on all kinds of beauty issues - from how to find the right foundation shade to ways of removing unwanted hair. Each query popping up in my inbox and each question thrown at me needs a bespoke and knowledgeable response.

A couple of years ago, it became clear to me that there was a real information gap out there. The need for a specific guide to cater for the modern South Asian woman and this was the motivating force behind my writing this book.

The Ultimate Guide to Beauty is a collation of everything I know (and in working on this book I have learnt so much), as well as invaluable advice and secrets from some of the world's leading experts in their respective fields. I hope that this book will prove to be a timeless and indispensable companion on your dressing table.

I am a self-confessed beauty junkie. I truly believe that there is nothing superficial about playing with your appearance or striving to improve it. Embracing beauty, through the way you live your life is nothing to be ashamed of and nor should it be perceived as vanity. Be it through simple lifestyle routines such as exercise and meditation, or enhancing your appearance with the use of treatments, creams and cosmetics, looking after and being interested in your skin, hair, body and inner being is all about respecting yourself.

This book is for all you girls who are confused, curious or like me, obsessed with beauty. It is your encyclopaedia into a fascinating and empowering world.

I am sure that all of you, no matter your age or country of residence, will find something amongst all the chapters here to appeal to you. I hope you enjoy reading and using it as much as I have enjoyed putting it together.

Anjana

A NOTE FOR THE READER

I regularly refer to many different experts in this book. To help you keep track of who they are, you may find it useful to refer to the Meet the Experts section on page 196.

BEAUTY THOUGH THE AGES

For as long as human history has been documented, women have sought ways to enhance their appearance and pursue an image of beauty. In many ancient civilizations, notably the Greeks, beauty was seen as a gift from the gods, and striving to be more attractive was an almost heavenly pursuit that brought one closer to the creator. Before the Greeks the ancient Egyptians had revolutionized the use of cosmetic tools and treatments. Scented oils, tinted powders and golden body paints were widely used by the women of the time.

Make-up, clearly, is no modern concept. In South Asia, archaeological work has unearthed ivory kohl eye sticks dating back to circa 600 BC, during the Vedic-Aryan period. Further on, in the rich annals of Asian history we find ample evidence of the use of cosmetics in all-important beauty rituals.

Fa-heen, a Chinese Buddhist monk who travelled in India during the Gupta period (around 300 AD) has described the fashion and beauty customs of the age. In his memoirs he observed that women would use red missi dye to darken their lips, and henna to redden the palms of their hands and soles of their feet.

In the wonderful, lavish paintings of the Mughal era, the use of cosmetics match the exuberance of the courts and flamboyance of regality. In these works of art it is virtually impossible to find an unpainted face. It was part of a woman's daily routine to look extraordinary. We see women depicted with voluptuous, hourglass figures, and lustrous long hair - looking almost flawless. Perhaps it should be of little surprise, that the greatest monument to love - the Taj Mahal - was built during this time.

No history of beauty is complete without a mention of India's most famous manuscript of love, the Kama Sutra, which is thought to have been originally compiled around 100 AD, by Vatsyayana. Its numerous artistic portrayals feature sensual and alluring women, with rouged lips, henna-stained toes and eyes lined seductively with kohl.

It is this rich canvas of history, which has inspired South Asian women for years. Here, perhaps more than anywhere else in the world, beauty customs are passed down adoringly from one generation to another. Whether it is flower petals in the bath, which are believed to soften the skin or specially-formulated oils used to nourish the hair, ours is truly a culture in which beauty traditions endure.

Today, we are able to combine the beauty rituals that have been in our families for centuries, with the very latest innovations in the beauty world. The growing demand, individuality and spending-power of the global South Asian woman, has led to more cosmetic houses finally widening their repertoire and directly catering to us. Beauty has never been so widely recognized, celebrated and appreciated.

Combining the authentic, exotic and almost mystical, beauty traditions of the East with the modern, innovative sensibilities of the West, we now have the best of both worlds and can present a truly contemporary image of our beauty to the world.

CHAPTER ONE
SKIN

SKIN

As smooth as silk, as fresh as a rose petal - writers have used these words to describe a woman's skin for centuries. Every woman strives for a clear flawless complexion and why shouldn't she? After all, the skin on the face and neck is the one area that is seen and noticed first.

Our skin is the largest functioning organ in our body. It protects our insides by excreting the body's toxic waste and absorbing oxygen. It reflects our skincare and lifestyle habits as well as our general health. The skin acts as the body's first line of defence against the environment. Besides the constant onslaught of pollution, it has to deal with the effects of sun, cold and humidity too. It is the first part of our body to show signs of stress and don't forget - it is also the frontline of our constant fight against signs of ageing. What we need to understand is that, no matter how great our skin is, it deserves constant tender loving care. A little time and effort will improve both its appearance and texture.

The ideal lifestyle plan for the skin should include a nutritious diet, plenty of water, regular exercise, adequate sleep and sensible stress management. If the skin balance becomes disturbed due to neglect, it can result in dryness, excessive oiliness, breakouts and it might also become incapable of offering protection against infection.

Having a daily skincare routine is essential to ensure that the complexion stays youthful and radiant. While technological advances have given us more and more skincare products to choose from, and regular facials help in improving our skin condition, there are however, no miracle cures. Nothing can protect the skin as much as a healthy lifestyle. Invest some time and effort and your skin will see the benefits.

GET TO KNOW YOUR SKIN

The first and most important step in achieving great skin is to identify your skin type and condition. Although our skin condition can change from one day to the next depending on internal factors (hormonal changes, health problems and use of medication) as well as external factors (changes in climate and exposure to the sun), for the majority of the time, we all have an underlying skin type.

FOUR COMMON SKIN TYPES

Dry skin
This type of skin lacks sebum production and moisture. Dry skin tends to be more prone to premature ageing. It can look patchy, fragile and there may even be a few visible expression lines. This skin type can also flake and chap easily.

Dry skin is actually thirsty skin that lacks moisture. This moisture needs to be replaced by a regular supply of water. Those with dry skin should drink at least eight glasses of water a day. Using the right products will feed the skin with emollient and moisture. An emollient will provide the skin with oils, keep it lubricated and trap in the moisture. The right moisturizer, used twice daily, will give skin a boost and increase the water content of the outer layers, giving it a soft and hydrated look. Cream-based cleansers are ideal for this skin type.

It is also important to choose the right make-up. Powder based products will only add to the dryness of the skin by sticking in every crease. Cream and oil-based products such as foundations and blushers, containing ingredients such as silicones, will glide on easily giving a better finish.

If you have dry skin, you should avoid overexposure to the sun, air conditioning and central heating. Washing your face with soap and water can also make the condition worse as it removes the natural oils that protect the skin. Cream-based cleansers are rich in texture and gentler on the skin. They leave behind a light veil of moisture and are far less harsher than soap and water.

Oily skin
Oily skin is the result of an overactive sebaceous (oil producing) gland, which basically means the skin produces more oil than is needed. Whilst it may act as a natural moisturizer, protecting against climate aggressors and keeping the skin looking youthful, supple and free from wrinkles, it also results in open pores and skin that is prone to breakouts, blackheads and acne.

The flow of sebum increases during teenage years and usually decreases with age. You may also notice a rise in the sebaceous gland activity during pregnancy and menopause.

If you're prone to oily skin, pay special attention to cleansing to keep the pores unclogged. You may find that water-based cleansers work best. Try not to over-cleanse, it may feel fresh for a moment, but over-stimulating the skin will only aggravate the sebaceous glands, which will then work overtime to produce even more sebum.

The staying power of your make-up may cause a problem here, but careful cosmetic choices can help. Choose make-up formulas and moisturizers that are 'oil-free'. Powder blushers and eye shadows will help to absorb excess oil and will also last longer than cream-based options. Try to avoid 'satin finish' or 'glossy' products, which contain silicones that can make the skin look greasy.

Combination skin

Combination skin has areas that are both dry and oily. This skin type is the most balanced and least problematic. You may find that your t-zone area tends to be oily while the skin around the eyes and cheeks could be dry. Unfortunately, there is no off-the-shelf cream that is perfect for both areas, so get used to buying different products. If this is impractical and costly you could use the same moisturizer, but apply a little more of it on the dry patches.

Choosing make-up for this skin type is fairly simple - there are no particular rules to stick to or ingredients to look out for or avoid. Just play around with make-up and go for whatever you feel comfortable using.

Sensitive skin

This skin type is prone to react to both heat and cold. It sunburns and windburns easily. It is commonly dry, delicate and inclined to allergic reactions, flare-ups and itchiness. Use of certain products can cause stinging, burning or breakouts. It is difficult to agree on a precise definition of sensitive skin, but if you find that yours reacts to products that most women have no problems with, then your skin may fall into this group.

Most of us will experience an allergic reaction at some point, but if you have skin that constantly flares up, it is best to treat it as you would treat dry skin conditions.

Tips to combat skin sensitivity

• Use moisturizers and sunscreens whenever the skin is going to be exposed to the sun and wind.
• Always carry out a make-up patch test prior to buying new products. Test the product on your inner elbow or on the skin behind the ear for a couple of days. If there is no problem, you can try it on the side of your face. If a reaction occurs, rinse the area with cold water and apply some soothing aloe vera gel.
• Look for products that are labelled hypoallergenic or allergy-tested, although even these do not guarantee against an adverse reaction.
• Avoid products that contain alcohol or surfactants. Do not over exfoliate or go for facials unless you are certain that the products used are suitable for your skin.

PROBLEM SKIN

Most of us will suffer from some kind of skin trouble in our lives. Here's how to deal with a less-than-perfect complexion.

Acne

What is acne? In a nutshell, acne is an inflammation of the sebaceous glands. Excess sebum (oil) blocks the hair follicles, often called pores. This sebum, which normally drains to the surface, gets trapped inside and causes spots and pimples to erupt.

The sebaceous glands are controlled by a hormone called androgens, the male hormone also found in women. For most people with acne, it begins at puberty. This is when the body starts to produce androgens, which causes the enlargement and over stimulation of the sebaceous glands. Sensitivity to these androgens also provokes acne to appear during the menstrual cycle and sometimes during pregnancy.

Treatment: Your doctor or dermatologist will usually suggest an over-the-counter prescription such as antibiotic creams or longer courses of oral antibiotics which are usually taken for a period of up to 12 weeks. In some cases hormone treatments may also be prescribed. Although they can be expensive, laser sessions have also been quite effective in zapping away spots, scars and redness.

Natural preventative methods such as a healthy diet can help in the war against acne. Include plenty of fruit, vegetables, salads and wholegrains in your diet.

Regular exercise can also work to beat acne, by helping you sleep better, fighting negative stress levels as well as boosting your metabolism and digestion.

Blackheads and whiteheads

Blackheads are caused when sebum collects and hardens in the pores. The toxins from the blood and lymph fluid that are being expelled through the skin, combines with sebum, creating a pasty glue. Due to oxidation, the tip turns black when exposed to air.

Whiteheads are follicles that are filled with the same substance, but have only a microscopic opening on the skin's surface. Since the air cannot reach the follicle, the material is not oxidized, and remains white.

Treatment: Never squeeze blackheads and whiteheads, as this may cause cross infection, which can lead to scarring. A good skincare regime and regular facials will definitely help. Facial steaming and pore cleansing strips can also assist with the removal of blackheads. Eliminate factors that can lead to clogged pores. Using oil based foundations and heavy moisturisers can increase your chances of developing blackheads.

Facial eczema

Eczema, or dermatitis as it is sometimes called, is a condition that can affect all age groups and its severity can vary. In mild forms the skin is dry, hot and itchy, whilst in more severe forms it can become broken, raw and bleeding. With treatment the inflammation of eczema can be reduced, though the skin will always be sensitive to flare-ups and would need extra care. Consult a dermatologist or qualified naturopath.

Red patches

Red patches on the skin are usually due to enlarged blood vessels. The term given to it is rosacea. Rosacea causes red bumps and facial flushing usually around the nose and cheek area.

Treatment: Avoid irritating factors that lead to flare-ups, such as alcohol, tobacco, spicy and citrus foods, hot drinks and sun exposure. Flare-ups of this nature may also occur during menopause. Vitamin B1 and B2 supplements, presription creams or antibiohcs can help reduce the symptoms. Consulting a dermatologist is best.

Hyperpigmentation

Hyperpigmentation is the darkening of an area of the skin caused by the body producing too much melanin. It often appears as darker patches usually found on the upper cheeks, nose or forehead. Although the condition can affect anyone, it is a common concern for those with darker skin tones.

The two most common types of hyperpigmentation are melasma and post inflammatory hyperpigmentation. Melasma causes dark, blotchy patches on the face, which tend to darken as they are exposed to the sun. Women taking birth control pills or hormone replacement therapy can also be prone to the condition. When it appears in pregnant women, it is often referred to as "the mask of pregnancy," or chloasma. This type of melasma usually fades several months after the baby is born.

Post inflammatory hyperpigmentation is caused by a response to a range of conditions such as infections, cosmetic treatments, acne and rashes including psoriasis and eczema.

Treatment: If you experience any form of hyperpigmentation, it is best to have the type and cause diagnosed by a doctor.

If the problem lies in the epidermis (the top layer of the skin), then topical (skin applied) treatments are usually recommended. If the problem lies deeper inside the second layer (the dermis), your doctor may suggest a suitable treatment.

Remember that sunlight stimulates melanin production so adequate year round sun protection is vital.

If you experience melasma whilst taking birth control pills, consult your doctor who may advise you to stop taking them or to switch brands.

Don't experiment with skin lightening products - many seemingly harmless products may contain ingredients that cause inflammation, which can make the problem worse.

10 STEPS TO BEAUTIFUL SKIN

1
Cleanse your skin twice daily

2
Always remove make-up before going to sleep

3
Avoid the sun - if this is not possible,
make sure you use a sunscreen

4
Quit smoking

5
Drink eight to ten glasses of water a day

6
Exercise on a regular basis

7
Eat plenty of fresh fruit and vegetables

8
Get adequate beauty sleep

9
Get to know your skin and treat it according to its needs

10
Oil production starts to slow down around the age of 25.
See a beauty therapist regularly and be ready to
make changes in your beauty regime.

THE PATH TO SKIN PERFECTION

SKINCARE

A daily skincare regime is an absolute must for long term skin health. It is also the biggest favour you can do for your complexion. Climate, age and stress are the main factors that cause the skin to change and these changes need to be dealt with in your daily beauty routine.

Cleansing

Cleansing should be the first and most essential step in your skincare regime. Use a cleanser before applying make-up, as it provides a clean and even canvas to work on. Whilst some insist that soap and water is the only way to cleanse others may argue that this old-school method is too harsh and can leave the skin dry and itchy. There are several, less harsher alternatives to soap and water. You can use water-based cleansers which are available in many forms such as bars, liquid and foam. These are milder and kinder to the complexion. If you have dry skin, then cream, oil or milk-based cleansers are great at removing dirt and grime as well as leaving behind a little moisture on the skin's surface.

Cleansing steps

1 Wash hands
2 Apply cleanser to the face in an upward and outward movement, ensuring not to stretch, drag or pull the skin.
3 Leave the cleanser on for a minute or two, to loosen the dirt and make-up.
4 Remove the cleanser with an upward and outward movement, using a cotton wool pad, muslin cloth or water (depending on the type of cleanser).

Toning

Toning is works to remove any residue left behind after cleansing. It also closes open pores thus giving the skin a smooth and clear texture. Some beauty experts say that toning is not a daily essential as it can cause a tightening and drying effect to the skin. However, if you feel your skincare regime is not complete without toning, then make sure you choose a product that is alcohol-free.

Anjana's Top Tip!

Remember to change your cleanser with the weather. Don't use the same bottle for more than eight to ten weeks as even skincare has a sell-by date – check with the counter staff before purchasing.

Moisturizing

A good moisturizer should perform a few basic functions. It should supply the skin with moisture, which will form a barrier between the skin and external aggressors. Whether your skin is dry, oily, combination or sensitive, its condition is certain to change depending on how it reacts to external factors (changing weather and harsh environmental conditions) and internal factors (fluctuating hormones and stress). These changes in condition are always different and specific to each individual.

All skin types need moisturizing. Feeding your skin with a suitable moisturizer is the only way to prevent it from becoming dehydrated and it should be an essential part of your daily routine.

Thanks to advances and innovations in skincare we are fortunate enough to be able to choose from hundreds of creams. Both mass-market and luxury brands give us plenty of options of products containing a whole host of ingredients in different textures.

When choosing a moisturizer it is important to know which type is best suited to your skin. The two main categories of moisturizers are humectants and occlusives. Those containing humectants will work to attract moisture from the atmosphere to the surface of the skin. Those containing occlusives (such as petroleum jelly and oils) will create an oily film on the surface of the skin. This will work to seal in moisture and prevent evaporation. Occlusive-based moisturizers are better suited for drier skin types.

The best time to apply your moisturizer is while the skin is damp. This is usually within three minutes of bathing, when the pores are open allowing moisture to lock in.

Exfoliation

Exfoliation works to give the complexion a perk by sloughing away dead surface cells and exposing fresh new ones. The shedding process unclogs pores and keeps clean. It also allows the moisturizer to penetrate better.

Eyes

The eye zone is one of the first to show signs of ageing through fine lines and wrinkles. Keeping the area hydrated is important. The trick is not to overdo product use around this area and stick to a light gel or cream formula. Apply product using a delicate, patting motion with your ring finger.

Neck

The neck and decolletage need to be taken care of just like the face, to prevent wrinkles and sagging. Start using a good moisturizer in your early twenties.

Lips

Our lips have no sebaceous glands which means they rely on external moisture to keep them in the right condition. Exposure to harsh weather conditions, be it the summer sun or winter winds, can make the lips dry, chapped and sore. They are particularly prone to dehydration due to our habit of constantly licking them. Smoking can also lead to lines appearing around the mouth. Lips need to be kept lubricated and hydrated with a protective non-petroleum based lip balm (as petroleum-based balms can become addictive).

Hands

The hands can easily give away your age, which is why it is worth looking after them. They are prone to dryness, lines and wrinkles so protect them with gloves when washing up or using household detergents. Investing in a good quality hand cream with added UV protection is also important.

AGEING SKIN

Research shows that there are two distinct types of ageing. Ageing caused by the genes we inherit is called intrinsic (internal) ageing. The other type of ageing is known as extrinsic (external) ageing and is caused by environmental factors, such as exposure to the sun's rays.

Intrinsic ageing, also known as the natural ageing process, is a continuous procedure that usually begins in our mid-20s. However, the signs of intrinsic ageing are typically not visible for decades. The most evident signs of intrinsic ageing are:

• Fine lines, especially around the eye area
• Thin and transparent skin
• Slack, greyish, pigmentation marks
• Loss of underlying fat, leading to hollowed cheeks and eye sockets, as well as noticeable loss of firmness on the hands and neck.

Why does the skin age?

To make sense of the skin's ageing process, it is important to know what it is essentially made up of. The skin has three layers. The top layer is called the epidermis and within the epidermis is melanin, which is what gives our skin its pigmentation. Melanin helps to protect us from the sun's rays. Under the epidermis is a much larger layer called the dermis, which has all the blood vessels, sweat glands and collagen fibres. These layers make up what we refer to as the skin. Underneath the dermis is the adipose tissue (otherwise known as fat). This is healthy fat and it gives our skin an even shape.

Environmental stresses cause the cells at the outer layer of the epidermis to wear out, but newer cells are already rising upwards (from the lower level of the epidermis) to replace the old cells. In young women this skin renewal process takes place every two to three weeks and in older women it takes up to twice as long.

As we become older, the outer layer of the epidermis becomes slightly thinner, and the cells that are being made at the lower level are dividing and replacing themselves at a slower pace. Therefore healing time is affected, along with a decrease in the production of newer skin cells. This reduction in new cells causes the skin to become thinner and we begin to notice some of the visible signs of ageing.

As we get older, the melanin-producing cells also decrease, which puts the skin at a higher risk of being damaged by the sun (as there is less pigment to protect it from ultraviolet light). From the age of 50, the number of elastin fibres declines causing drooping and sagging - in other words that plumpness and firmness begin to deplete. The level of oil production also decreases causing the skin to become dry.

A number of extrinsic, or external, factors can cause premature ageing. Smoking, caffeine, alcohol and lack of sleep play a huge role, as do environmental aggressors such as sun exposure.

But it is not all doom and gloom from here and luckily science and technological breakthroughs are working in our favour.

If you practice good skincare throughout your early years you will have a better chance of maintaining a healthier and youthful looking complexion through later life, but it's never too late to start. So take extra care and your skin will respond quickly and positively.

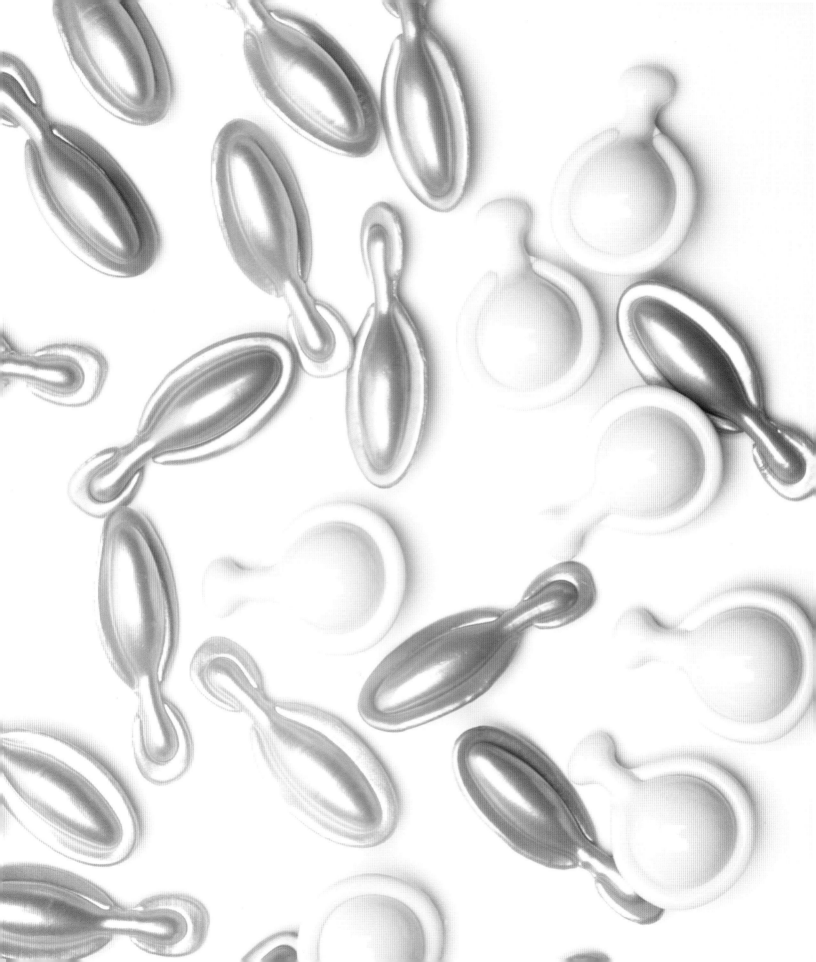

INGREDIENTS IN BEAUTY PRODUCTS

What makes up your lotions and potions?

Have you ever read the labels of your favourite products and wondered what all those ingredients actually do? Well, here's a crash course through the beauty jargon so you are no longer left wondering.

Alpha-Hydroxy Acids (AHAs)

These are one of the most significant discoveries in the fight against ageing. Derived from natural ingredients, including grapes, apples, olives and milk, AHAs work by retexturizing and gently dissolving the 'intercellular glue' that holds together the dead cells to the surface of the skin. They uncover new layers of skin and moisturize these. They are thought to be beneficial to complexions that have started to look dull, dry or flaky by giving skin a plumper and more youthful appearance. However, they can prove too harsh for sensitive and delicate skins.

Antioxidants

The antioxidants used in cosmetics and skincare are derived mainly from vitamins A, C and E as well as beta-carotene. These are all used in face creams and are thought to protect the skin against attacks from free radicals, which are triggered by exposure to the sun, pollution and cigarette smoke.

Beta Hydroxy Acids (BHAs)

These work in a similar way to AHAs. The main difference is their lipid (oil) solubility. AHAs are water soluble only, while BHAs are lipid soluble, which means they are able to penetrate into the pores that contain sebum and exfoliate the dead skin cells that are built up inside. They are commonly used to treat acne.

Ceramides

These are lipids that help to prevent moisture loss by stabilizing the skin's structure. They assist the skin in its function as an efficient barrier and are beneficial to all of us - especially for older, dry or damaged skins. They are naturally found in healthy skin but dry skin types may be deficient in them.

Collagen/Elastin

These are the fibres that give our skin firmness and elasticity. As we age the production of collagen and elastins begins to slow down causing the skin to become loose and appear less supple. Products containing collagen can act as a surface moisturizer to the skin.

Enzymes

Enzymes are used in skincare ingredients such as moisturizers and masks. They work by gently removing dead cells on the skin's outer layer without causing any irritation or harm to living cells.

Glycolic Acid

A natural acid found in sugarcane, glycolic acid is useful in aiding the exfoliation of dead skin cells and is usually found in anti-ageing products that help promote softer and younger looking skin. It is also known to have hydrating and moisturizing properties.

Humectants

Humectants work by attracting moisture from the surrounding atmosphere to the surface of the skin. Glycerin and sorbitol are the most commonly used in moisturizers and are effective in the treatment of dry skin.

Kaolin

Kaolin is a fine white powder made from natural clay. It has exceptional sebum absorbing properties and is found in facial masks for oily skin types.

Keratin

Keratin is a tough, fibrous protein that makes up the skin, hair and nails. It is often found in shampoos and hair-care products where it is used as a strengthener.

Licorice extract

Licorice comes from a plant that is a member of the 'legume' family and is historically used in skin preparations to diminish the look of 'age spots'. Recent studies indicate that it appears to have a de-pigmenting effect and may help inhibit melanin formation.

Lipids

Lipids are fatty acids that play an important part in the retention of moisture in the skin by helping to absorb active ingredients.

Liposomes

Liposomes are tiny sacs that deliver hydrating ingredients to skin cells. It is believed that they are tiny enough to penetrate deep into the epidermis and enable the skin cells to hold water more effectively.

Retinoids

Retinoids are a derivative of vitamin A. They come in different forms such as retin-A, retinol, retinova and renova, and they are often used in acne and anti-ageing treatments. The disadvantage is that they make the skin hypersensitive to sunlight. Aggressive treatments such as waxing should be avoided while using these creams.

Vitamin C

Vitamin C is used in various skincare products as it is an extremely powerful ingredient, with high antioxidant properties. It works to boost the collagen production in the skin, which helps to slow down the formation of fine lines and wrinkles.

pH

This is a term often seen on packaging. It means percentage of hydrogen and is commonly used to measure acidity in cosmetic preparations. A healthy skin is slightly acidic and should have a pH between 4.5 and 5.5. The skin's pH balance can be disturbed by the use of soaps which are usually strongly alkaline.

Panthenol/Pro vitamin B5

Derived from vitamin B and known for its revitalizing and highly conditioning effects, panthenol is a non-irritating ingredient often used in hair and skincare products.

Peptides

Peptides are one of the newest ingredients to hit the skincare scene. They work by penetrating deep inside the skin to stimulate the development of new collagen. When topically applied over time, it can noticeably increase skin thickness and improve the appearance of ageing skin.

Salicylic acid

The most common BHA (beta hydroxy acid), which is cosmetically used in some chemical peels and in products to reduce oiliness and acne.

Titanium dioxide

A broad spectrum physical UV blocker that is added to sunscreens to help deflect both UVA and UVB light.

Witch Hazel

A botanical with astringent properties, which work to remove excess surface skin oils.

Yeast Extract

This ingredient is extracted from brewer's yeast and contains a complex mixture of proteins, sugars, vitamins and amino acids. Some claim that it may enhance the rate of renewal (cell turnover) of the skin.

BE SAFE IN THE SUN

In the subcontinent, there was a time when women with fairer skin were perceived as being healthier, wealthier and more attractive by default. Thankfully, this old-fashioned attitude is fading fast, and women with duskier skin tones are deemed just as desirable and beautiful, as their fair-skinned counterparts.

Most South Asian women are brown in skin tone and a little sun-kissed glow can add a healthy looking golden hue to our complexions. Most of us will find that skin-burning does not affect us as much as it does those with pale or white skin. In fact, the darker your skin is the more resistant you are to the damaging effects of the sun. Darker skins are blessed with higher levels of epidermal melanin, which provides us with a natural skin protection factor (SPF) making us less susceptible to sunburn, however this doesn't mean we are immune. Melanoma (the deadliest form of skin cancer) can strike dark-skinned people too, and when it does, it's more deadly because it's likely to be detected much later.

The onslaught of sun damage, over a prolonged period of time, can be more damaging than you think. UVA rays are 20 times more prevalent in the earth's atmosphere than skin burning UVB rays and they are the same strength all year round. It appears that UVA can penetrate through clothing, hats, tinted glass and office windows potentially causing silent destruction to the skin throughout the year.

These deeper penetrating rays cause irreversible damage to the skins structure. Collagen fibres give strength and elastin gives elasticity. Over years of sun exposure, the collagen and especially the elastin become damaged and the cells in the dermis become less able to repair this damage. So the skin loses its firmness and elasticity, and becomes wrinkled.

Frightening as it may sound, some care and protection can prevent the skin from being damaged.

Anjana's Top Tip!
Remember that in the case of sun exposure, less is best.

EXPERT TIPS

Follow these tips from Dr. Aparna Santhanam, Head of Medical Services at the Kaya Skin Clinic, to be safe in the sun

• The sun's rays are strongest between 10 am - 4 pm. During these hours keep your exposure to the sun to a minimum.

• Make sure that you never burn. Skin burning is our body's chemical response to over-exposure to UV rays. Experts believe that sunburn during childhood can significantly increase your risk of melanoma. Some say your chances of developing this type of skin cancer are doubled by just one blistering sunburn before the age of 20.

• Wear sunglasses to protect your eyes from the glare of the sun. Those that provide 99-100 per cent UVA and UVB protection will greatly reduce the risk of eye damage.

• When on a holiday, the general medical recommendation is to avoid tanning. However, if you must, always use protection. The SPF (sun protection factor) of a sunscreen is a measure of its ability to filter out UVB rays. When used correctly you will get over 90 per cent protection from UVB rays with SPF 15. Remember that no sunscreen - no matter how high the factor - can offer 100 per cent protection. Look for labeling such as full spectrum, broad spectrum and broad band - these offer both UVB (SPF) and UVA defence. When swimming outdoors opt for a water resistant formula, which is less likely to wash away or be sweated off.

• Give sunscreen plenty of time to absorb by applying it at least 15 minutes before exposure. Use a generous amount - studies show we use only half to one third of the amount of sunscreen needed to get the SPF on the label.

• Use a sunscreen with a high enough SPF. The higher the number, the greater the level of protection offered by the product. Reapply every two hours. If swimming, reapply every 40 minutes.

• Wear a higher SPF factor on your face than you do on your body. This is the area, which needs the most protection.

• Do not forget to apply it to all exposed skin areas, including the feet, front of hands and ears.

• If you do get sunburned, apply some soothing aloe vera gel to cool the area and help prevent damage. Take lukewarm rather than hot baths and showers.

• Use hydrating and moisturizing creams to replace moisture lost during sun exposure.

• Don't forget that your hair can also be affected. Use a deep conditioner to treat your locks at least once a week.

JET-LAGGED SKIN

• Flying can cause the skin to become extremely dehydrated, due to the fact that cabin air is drier than the deserts of Rajasthan! Follow these tips to make sure you touchdown with fresh looking skin.

• If you feel thirsty, don't ignore it. It's a sign of your body telling you that you are dehydrated. Drink plenty of water before, during and after the flight to keep your body and skin hydrated.

• Avoid drinking coffee and alcohol. Both can be extremely dehydrating to the skin. Carbonated fizzy drinks can cause stomach upsets and make you feel bloated.

• Keep your skin hydrated at all times. Use a moisturizer to ensure that it retains its water levels throughout the flight, it's a good idea to use one that is slightly richer than your regular face cream. Try using a night cream or a moisturising face mask during the flight.

• Carry a moisturising facial mist in your hand luggage and spritz over the face when the skin begins to feel thirsty.

• Keep the area around the eyes well hydrated and protected with an eye cream or gel - this fragile zone is the first to show signs of dehydration and ageing.

• Avoid wearing make-up or keep it to a minimum - it can cause a tightening effect on the skin, not to mention the fact that it might look awful by the time you land.

• Prevent water retention and a sluggish circulation by walking up and down the aisle as often as possible.

• After the flight, treat your skin to a good exfoliation to get rid of dirt and grime.

CHAPTER TWO
GET TO KNOW YOUR FACE

FACE SHAPES

Understanding your face shape and bone structure can do wonders for boosting your beauty potential. The shape of your face will influence the way you style yourself, cut your hair and apply make-up to accentuate your features.

We spend vast amounts of money on cosmetics, but this might all be going to waste if we are not using this make-up in the right way to compliment our face shape. We all have different facial features and this gives us individuality. Use this graphic to identify your face shape and guide you to make the right choices.

FIND YOUR FACE SHAPE
Oval

Oval faces are longer than they are wider. In this face shape the features are well balanced and generally even looking, almost symmetrical.

Famous oval faces: Jennifer Lopez, Aishwarya Rai.

Heart

The classic heart-shaped face is defined by wide cheekbones, which narrow down to a delicate yet pointy chin.

Famous heart faces: Jennifer Aniston, Lara Dutta.

Square

Square faces are recognized by their angular jaw line. The cheekbones are broad and equal in width to the jaw and hairline.

Famous square faces: Renée Zellweger, Preity Zinta

Long

Often defined by a prominent jaw, long faces are slim and characteristically include a high forehead and a well-defined, long chin.

Famous long faces: Iman, Priyanka Chopra.

Round

Round faces are full cheeked and circular (they tend to be as wide as they are long), usually combined with a small, pert nose. Round faces are associated with a youthful look. Those of you with this face shape may often get called 'baby face'.

Famous round faces: Catherine Zeta-Jones, Rani Mukherjee.

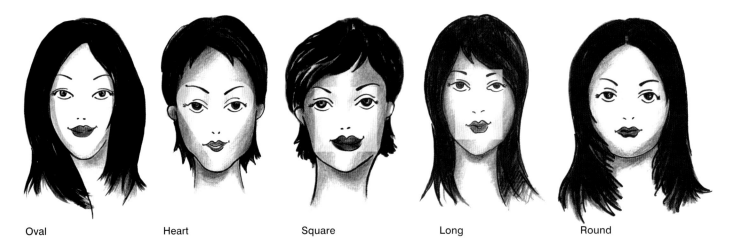

Oval   Heart   Square   Long   Round

GET TO KNOW YOUR FACE

Getting to know your face structure -
the canvas you are working on -
makes the task of make-up application
a lot simpler. Throughout this book
you will read constant references to
specific parts of the face on which to
apply make-up. This guide labels the
most prominent facial features for
make-up application. Why not take a
few minutes to grab a mirror and
identify them on your face?

hairline

temple

brow
brow bone
eyelid crease
lashline
inner rim of the eyelid

under eye area
cheekbone
bridge of nose
apple of the cheek

ball of the nose

lipline

jawline

tip of the chin

PROFESSIONAL SHADING TRICKS

Shading and highlighting is a make-up trick commonly used by the pros to minimize features their clients are not so happy with. If done correctly it is one of the most effective ways of enhancing or changing the features without going under the cosmetic knife. Make-up artist Nina Haider says, "The simple rule is to use dark colours to make the features recede and light colours to bring areas out."

Shading secrets

Apply your foundation base as normal - shading and highlighting products should always be applied over foundation. Remember that these techniques are best left for evening use - highlighting and shading can look far too harsh for daytime light.

To minimize the forehead

Apply a small amount of colour along the hairline to help minimize the appearance of a long forehead. Blend in the colour using a medium-sized brush to avoid an unnatural finish. Try to skip this look in the sun - the last thing you want is smudging.

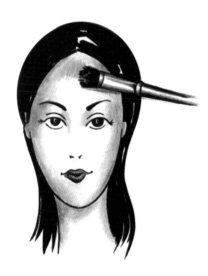

Clever hair styling and cutting can also help to detract attention from the forehead. Avoid scrapped back styles and opt for soft layers along the side of the face.

To slim a wide nose

1 Use clever highlighting and shading to create a slimmer nose. Apply a light non-shimmery highlighter using a soft-haired brush along the bridge of the nose.

2 Use a darker colour to contour the nose on either side. Remember to go easy on the colour application.

To make a long nose appear shorter

Apply a darker powder or a touch of bronzer on the tip of the nose.

To make a round face slender

Sweep some shading colour over the temples and under the cheekbones in addition to the jaw line and the area under the chin. Use a fluffy brush to highlight the centre of the forehead, the bridge of the nose and tip of the chin.

CHAPTER THREE
BEAUTY TOOLS

TOOLS

When applying make-up, using the correct tools can help ensure the best results. Having a good core selection of equipment, is a must for enhancing eyes, cheeks, lips or brows.

Brushes are now easily accessible and affordable. Every woman's basic make-up bag should include at least a handful of them. Using the correct brush will allow for the best possible results in make-up application.

Make-up kits used by professionals usually consist of around 15-20 brushes. But most make-up artists would agree, that they could get the job done with half that number. Invest in six or seven essential brushes and you too can achieve an immaculate make-up finish.

THE SEVEN HERO BRUSHES
The vital tools that every girl should have.

The powder brush
A good quality powder brush will give a delicate dusting to the face. Powder brushes are used to dust powder onto the face after foundation application to ensure longer staying power and a shine-free complexion. Choose a brush that is medium in size rather than one that has bristles the size of your palm. Make sure the bristles are firm, if they are too flimsy they won't wipe away excess powder effectively.

Powder Brush

Eyeliner Brush

The eyeliner brush
The eyeliner brush should have a synthetic head. The flexibility and soft fine tip of this brush makes it easy to follow the curvature of the eye and delivers a precise, firm and thin line. This brush is ideally used with liquid or cream products. Depending on your liner preference, the other type of eyeliner brush is one that is more commonly used to apply powder shadow as liner at the base of the lashes. This brush has a small, firm and flat tip with bristles that are densely packed together, so that colour can be directed exactly where you want it.

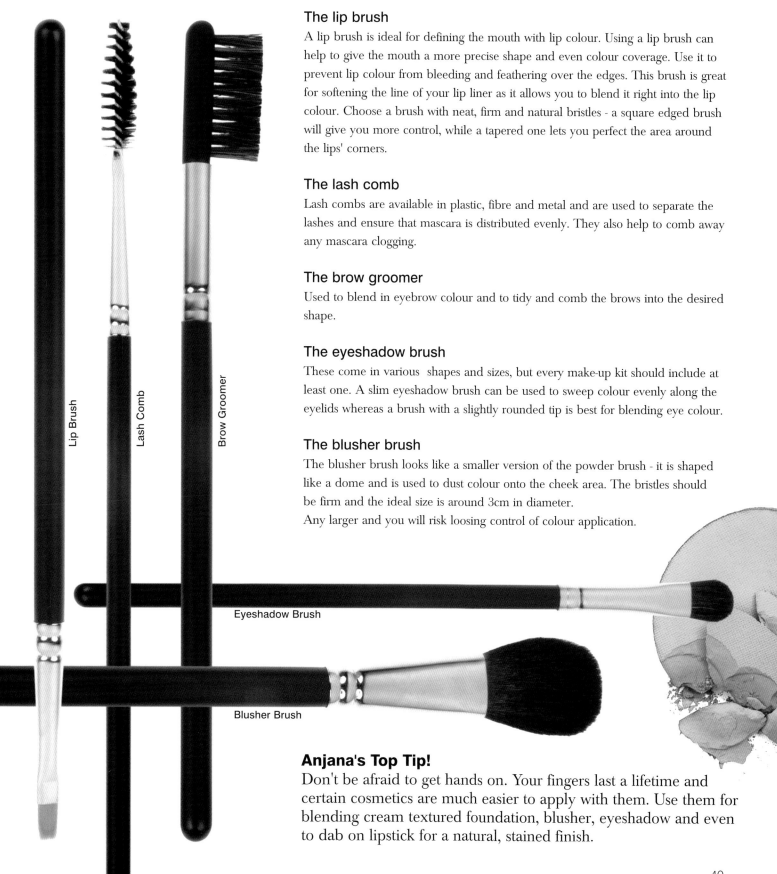

The lip brush

A lip brush is ideal for defining the mouth with lip colour. Using a lip brush can help to give the mouth a more precise shape and even colour coverage. Use it to prevent lip colour from bleeding and feathering over the edges. This brush is great for softening the line of your lip liner as it allows you to blend it right into the lip colour. Choose a brush with neat, firm and natural bristles - a square edged brush will give you more control, while a tapered one lets you perfect the area around the lips' corners.

The lash comb

Lash combs are available in plastic, fibre and metal and are used to separate the lashes and ensure that mascara is distributed evenly. They also help to comb away any mascara clogging.

The brow groomer

Used to blend in eyebrow colour and to tidy and comb the brows into the desired shape.

The eyeshadow brush

These come in various shapes and sizes, but every make-up kit should include at least one. A slim eyeshadow brush can be used to sweep colour evenly along the eyelids whereas a brush with a slightly rounded tip is best for blending eye colour.

The blusher brush

The blusher brush looks like a smaller version of the powder brush - it is shaped like a dome and is used to dust colour onto the cheek area. The bristles should be firm and the ideal size is around 3cm in diameter.
Any larger and you will risk loosing control of colour application.

Lip Brush

Lash Comb

Brow Groomer

Eyeshadow Brush

Blusher Brush

Anjana's Top Tip!

Don't be afraid to get hands on. Your fingers last a lifetime and certain cosmetics are much easier to apply with them. Use them for blending cream textured foundation, blusher, eyeshadow and even to dab on lipstick for a natural, stained finish.

AND THE SIDEKICKS...

They may not be your absolute essentials, but for a kit to be proud of, these useful tools are worth the investment.

The powder puff

Powder puffs are great for precise touch ups, especially with evening make-up where coverage is usually heavier and the look is more glamorous. Invest in one that is soft and medium in size.

The sponge

These are brilliant for blending and suitable to use with most foundation textures. Wedge-shaped sponges are great at reaching those awkward areas around the nose and eyes.

The tweezers

A product that is found in every girl's make-up bag. Whether you wax, thread or tweeze your brows, a pair of tweezers is a must have to tidy up unruly strays and pluck away unwanted growth.

The foundation brush

This handy brush is great for creating an even and well-blended finish, especially when using liquid or cream foundation. The professional ones can be expensive, but if taken care of, they can last for years.

The concealer brush

This flat, tapered brush helps guide liquid or cream concealer over blemishes. Usually made from synthetic bristles, it will glide smoothly across the area ensuring even and precise product distribution.

Powder Puff

Sponge

Sponge

Tweezer

Foundation Brush

Natural or Synthetic Brushes

Natural bristle brushes are "scaled" which makes them ideal for holding powder pigments, (such as eyeshadow, loose powder and blusher) more effectively. These brushes can be made from single animal fibres or a mix. The formation process involves the fibres being grouped together, colour matched, and bound into a brush. It is a lengthy process, which is part of the reason why they are so expensive.

Synthetic brushes are less expensive and are perfect for use with creamy products such as lipstick, concealer and cream eyeliner. They are not suitable for use with powdered cosmetics, as the powder will not grip to the bristles effectively.

Skip the tools

Don't be afraid to get hands on. Your fingers last a lifetime and certain cosmetics are much easier to apply with them. Make-up artists are regularly seen using their fingers to swipe, smudge and smear. You may have noticed that most cream and gel formulations come without an applicator and these products are ideal for dabbing on with the fingers. Use them for blending cream blusher, eyeshadow and even to dab on lipstick for a natural, stained finish.

Due to the natural heat our skin produces, the fingers can be the ultimate tool for blending concealer, especially for sensitive areas like under the eyes.

Anjana's Top Tip!

Try before you buy. Test the brush out with the type of product you intend to use it on.

CARING FOR YOUR BRUSHES

It is important to clean your brushes to maintain their condition and to keep them as hygienic as possible.

How often should I wash my brushes?
If you use the same basic colours on a daily basis then washing them once every two months should be enough. Washing natural hair brushes too often can break down the shaft and loosen the glue that holds the handle and bristles together.

What should I use to wash my brushes?
Use a mild and gentle shampoo such as Johnson's Baby Shampoo. Make sure the shampoo you use is free of conditioning agents.

How to clean your brushes

1   Grab a small bowl and half fill it with lukewarm water and a capful of mild shampoo.
    Swish brushes around, gently separating the bristles until all the pigment is removed.

2   Rinse the brush thoroughly, until the water runs clear.

3   Gently press out any excess water from the bristles and dab the brush dry on a towel.

4   Finally, use your hands to arrange the bristles back into their original shape and let it air-dry overnight.

CHAPTER FOUR
FOUNDATION

SKIN TONE

Originating from the same part of the world does not mean that we all have the same skin colour. Some of us are fair skinned, some are mid-tones and some are dusky. Today, the growth in interracial relationships has made a "typical" skin-tone even less easy to identify, with many people having a more diverse and exotically-coloured complexion.

There was a time when ethnic women were frustrated by a woeful lack of make-up choice. Cosmetic houses had their signature two or three shades to cater for our skin-tone, and they naively believed that one of these would compliment our skin. As we all know now - they were wrong.

These days, thanks to technological advances, the increased demand and extensive research, the spectrum of colours and textures on offer has greatly improved. International cosmetic houses are getting their act together by developing an even more diverse range for us to choose from and thankfully the majority of us are sure to find a shade to match our complexion.

Foundation expert Farah Naz says:

"The first priority when choosing make-up for our skin tones is to ensure that it has a yellow base. This works with the natural undertones of our skin, helping to enhance rather than mask the complexion. If make-up designed for Caucasian skin tones is used then the results can either be orange or chalky, leaving a mask-like finish that works against the natural tone."

Here's a simple way to figure out your skin tone:

What would happen to your skin if it were exposed to the sun for an hour, without any protection? If it tans, freckles or just stays the same, which is usually the case for most South Asians, then your complexion is warm and needs a foundation shade with a yellow-tinge ('honey' or 'golden' is usually in the name). If you have fair skin that turns bright pink in the sun, your skin probably has a cool tone, so opt for foundations with 'ivory' or 'beige' in the name.

FOUNDATION

Once upon a time women would camouflage their complexion by using sticks of bintsuke wax (a softer version of the sumo wrestlers' hair wax). Others used white paste and powder. Women wanted the "real white" look, which was created by applying chalk or white lead face powder.

Today's developments and changes in attitudes mean that we no longer want to camouflage or disguise our skin. Instead we want bases that will enhance our natural skin tone. Most of us have a wide range to choose from, but those of you who still find it difficult to find the perfect match, should perhaps opt for a custom-blended foundation.

The choice of formulas and textures are so vast that we can now use a separate foundation for different times of the day or to suit a particular occasion. For example, we can use light-responsive foundations for day-to-day wear or photochromic for special evenings out. Today's foundations come packed full of sun protecting, moisturizing and anti-ageing ingredients enabling you to select one that not only compliments your skin tone, but also meets your skin's needs.

Foundation is the blank canvas on which we apply the rest of our make-up. It is the base for any colour application. It conceals imperfections and embellishes and evens out the complexion. The key is to find a foundation that goes unnoticed, and gives a natural looking finish.

The endless choice of textures and colours can be overwhelming and confusing , but understanding your skin type and tone is essential in making the job easier.

CHOOSING THE RIGHT TEXTURE

Finding the right formula for your skin will help you create the perfect base for the rest of your make-up.

Cream foundations are creamy in texture and give a more intense, heavier coverage - perfect for when you want your skin to look velvety. Cream foundations keep the skin moisturized, but need a lot of blending. This texture is ideal for dry and mature skin-types, but can be too heavy for oily skin.

Compact foundations are all-in-one products with a creamy yet powdery texture. They work well with most skin tones and glide on easily with a sponge. They are portable and great for when you are on the go and need quick coverage.

Liquid foundations are probably the most versatile and suit most skin types. They provide sheer, lightweight and natural-looking coverage. They glide on easily and are available in oil and water-based formulas. Oil-based foundations are great for dry and wrinkled skin, making the complexion appear moist and dewy. Water-based formulas glide on effortlessly and leave behind a hint of sheen.

Oil-free and matte foundation gives the skin an even and shine-proof coverage. They stay shine-free for much longer than most other foundation types and are great for those with oily skin who want to achieve a smooth and matte look.

Cake or pan stick foundations are solid in form and give good coverage with a matte yet creamy finish. Due to their texture, they can also be used as a concealer for disguising scars and blemishes. These foundations are recommended for occasional use when you want to conceal specific flaws. Professional make-up artists often use pan sticks for photoshoots and fashion shows.

Tinted moisturizers offer the skin a minimal 'barely-there' finish, with a hint of colour. They help to keep the skin hydrated, but cannot conceal blotches or blemishes as well as other foundation textures can. Tinted moisturizers are great for any skin type that needs a hint of colour rather than full-on coverage. Blend well to avoid patching.

Mineral foundation has a fine powder like texture and feels almost weighless on the skin. It is easy to apply - simply empty a little powder into the lid, swirl the brush into the product then tap away any excess and blend into the skin. It can take a while to build up product to optimum coverage. It is made from 100 per cent natural ingredients including zinc, titanium, pearl, mica and gold. It's oil, fragrance and synthetic free formulation is non comedogenic, which means it won't clog the pores and the added zinc and titanium dioxide work as natural anti-inflammatories, which soothe sensitive skin. Its powdery consistency may leave dry skin a little flaky.

Airbrush foundation is a fairly new creation, and its use in the professional beauty circuit is increasing every day. The formula can last the entire day with no need for touch-ups. It creates a virtually flawless finish that blends beautifully into the skin. Airbrushes can be adjusted to be very soft and light to heavier in their application.

TYPES OF COVERAGE

Dewy
This type offers sheer coverage and gives skin a glowy appearance. It's ideal for those of you with good skin that only require minimal cover-up.

Matte
This is ideal for oily-skin types as it does not reflect light and gives the skin a matte finish.

Full coverage
This is ideal for those with not-so-perfect skin. The opaque coverage is heavy enough to disguise imperfections such as scars and birthmarks.

Pore-minimizing
This type reduces the appearance of pores by deflecting light from imperfections. It also helps control oil production.

Oil-free
This water-based formulation is ideal for oily skins. It includes silicone particles instead of moisturizing elements to ensure ease of application.

Two-in-one
This is a versatile base that can be applied dry for a lighter, silky finish or wet, for greater coverage.

Sheer
This is best for those with an almost blemish-free complexion, as it offers a light finish to even out the skin tone.

FOUNDATION LANGUAGE

The ingredients in your foundation work to make your complexion look perfect, but choosing the right one can be confusing. Look out for these words on the label to help you find one that works for your skin.

Silicones
These work to ensure easy application as they let the foundation glide on smoothly, giving a silky finish.

SPF
These help to protect against the ageing affects of the sun's UV rays.

Light-reflecting pigments
If these are found in your foundation, they will give an illusion of younger-looking skin.

Antioxidants
These help to keep the skin supple by boosting the production of collagen.

EXPERT TIPS
Farah Naz shares her knowledge of foundation.
- South Asian skin can be oily and prone to spots and outbreaks. The cosmetics used on this type of skin will affect its condition and an oil-free foundation is ideal.
- A matte foundation is essential for oily skins as it can minimise shine. Applying a dusting of finely milled powder will take away any shine and leave a fresh finish.
- Brown skin is more prone to scarring - the darker the skin the more this applies. Hyperpigmentation can occur around any sight of inflammation including acne. Prevention is better than cure so choose an oil-free foundation.

FINDING YOUR COLOUR MATCH

Choosing the right shade of foundation is the perfect way to achieve flawless skin. It needs to blend seamlessly into the jawline so as not to leave a mask-like finish.

Many South Asian women make the mistake of buying foundations that are too pink and as a result end up with an unnaturally flushed look, which sometimes appears grey and extremely unflattering.

Our skin tones can vary greatly, from very fair to dusky. However, we all share the same natural yellow undertones. It is important that we choose a foundation with a yellow base that works with the natural undertones of our skin.

Shop floor colour test

1 Remove any existing make-up as you can only judge the best shade on bare skin.

2 Select two or three colours that are as close as possible to your skin tone.

3 Always test foundation on the face and not on the hand as the skin tone may be different here. Apply the three most suitable shades in streaks across the jawline - this area offers the truest facial colouring. Gently blend in the colour, if it disappears into the skin, then this shade is right for you. When blending the colour, there should be no visible line between the jawbone and neck. If you find that you are in between two shades, mix these colours together or look for a brand that offers your perfect match.

4 Do not make a colour decision in artificial light. Lighting in department stores can be deceptive and distorting. Judge the colour in natural daylight to avoid any nasty surprises.

5 Let the colour settle into your skin before you decide to buy. The acid balance in the skin can change the colour of the foundation - so let it settle for half-an-hour or so to see how it reacts.

EXPERT TIPS

Foundation do's and don'ts by make-up maestro Mickey Contractor
- DO take your time to choose the right tone and texture of foundation to suit your skin's lifestyle and needs.
- DON'T wear excess foundation. It will only make you look older and accentuate wrinkles, especially after a few hours when the foundation starts to settle into fine lines.
- DO blend foundation into the skin. Blending is an art, which doesn't take long to master. Wear your foundation at home a couple of times and learn to blend well before you decide to go out with it.
- DON'T overdo it - use foundation sparingly so your skin's health shows through. If you have a clear and healthy-looking complexion, I have two words for you - flaunt it!
- DO use a buffer brush (MAC's #187 is simply amazing) after foundation as this is a good way to achieve an evenly-polished complexion.
- DO blend your foundation into the neck area.
- DON'T forget my motto - less is more.

COVERAGE COMMANDS

How to get picture-perfect coverage

Mickey Contractor shares his secret steps to achieving superstar coverage.

"Choosing the right foundation is half your battle won," says Mickey. "Once you find the correct shade, it's only by trial and error that you can actually apply your base flawlessly."

1 Start by applying moisturizer - this is a must for all skin types. If you live in warmer climates, I suggest you wear a water-based moisturizer under your make-up. For those living in colder climates, a slightly richer one is ideal.

2 Spread the foundation evenly over the face using your fingertips, a sponge or a brush. This really depends on what you are most comfortable with. I use my fingertips to blend foundation. Do not forget to blend well around the nostrils, under the eyes and into the neck area.

3 Some foundation textures do not need powder to set, but if yours does, lightly dust some translucent powder over the face using a brush or puff.

How to get a dewy base

Make-up artist Leena Jotangia tells us how to achieve a fresh, glowing complexion.

"To achieve a dewy finish, steer clear of foundations with a high powder concentration. Avoid oil-free or heavy-based matte textures," says Leena.

1 Prep the skin by cleansing, toning and moisturizing. This will ensure that the foundation has a perfect surface to sit on.

2 Apply a primer with the fingers starting from the nose and blending outwards. The primer will ensure that the foundation stays in place for longer.

3 Use your fingers to apply the foundation, (if you prefer a brush or sponge can be used) starting from the nose and blending outwards to avoid streaking.

My secret tip for achieving a dewy look is to mix the foundation with a touch of brightening serum. It gives the skin a beautiful pearlescent, fresh and radiant glow. Avoid using a moisturizer to achieve the same effect as you could end up looking greasy rather than dewy.

For a longer-lasting dew for the evening, use a powder puff to pat some finely milled loose powder over the top of the foundation. Buff the powder into the skin using circular movements with a powder brush. This brings a beautiful lustre to the skin and ensures a longer lasting base.

To glam up your dewy-foundation base, apply a highlighter over the cheekbones, brow bones, down the length of the nose, and a touch in the middle of the lips. My favourite product is, the Multiple Highlighter by NARS in Copacabana and Maldives shades.

Base in the sun

Make-up artist Clint Fernandes gives us his tips on how to achieve a melt-free base

- When exposed to the heat we naturally sweat and this causes make-up to melt away. In a hot climate, it is best to use as little foundation as possible. Ideally, try to avoid wearing it altogether and opt for a tinted moisturizer instead.
- The sun gives the skin a natural glow and evens out the complexion so avoid use of foundation and go for a stick concealer, which is a little more resistant to slipping. Use it only where necessary, to cover spots, blemishes or under-eye circles. Finish with a dust of translucent powder.
- Always carry a compact powder whilst you are out and about. It will come in handy when you need to combat the shiny and oily zones.

Minimize open pores

Open pores are caused by enlarged sebaceous glands secreting sebum onto the surface of the skin. These are usually visible around the nose and cheeks. It is difficult to completely get rid of them, but there are ways to minimize them.

Primer

Make-up artist Leena Jotangia says: "Primers give the skin a smooth, even surface on which to apply foundation - they work to tighten the pores and improve skin elasticity. An application of primer will allow your foundation to stay put for longer as well as stopping the base from changing colour, going patchy or just disappearing throughout the day. You may think it's an extra beauty expense, but they are sure worth a try for those occasions when you really need your make-up to last the distance."

Steaming

Shenaz Shariff from The Face & Body Clinic says: "Facial steaming is a natural and efficient way to improve the condition of the skin by opening and unblocking pores. The warmth opens pores and the moisture encourages the removal of impurities from under the skin's surface. If any blackheads need extracting, facial steaming helps the process by softening the skin and allowing greater access to the blocked pores."

Shenaz adds, "A toner can also be effective as it is an astringent and helps to close the pores following the cleansing process - this is very important as it minimizes the chances of further grime infiltrating below the skin's surface, creating spots and blackheads."

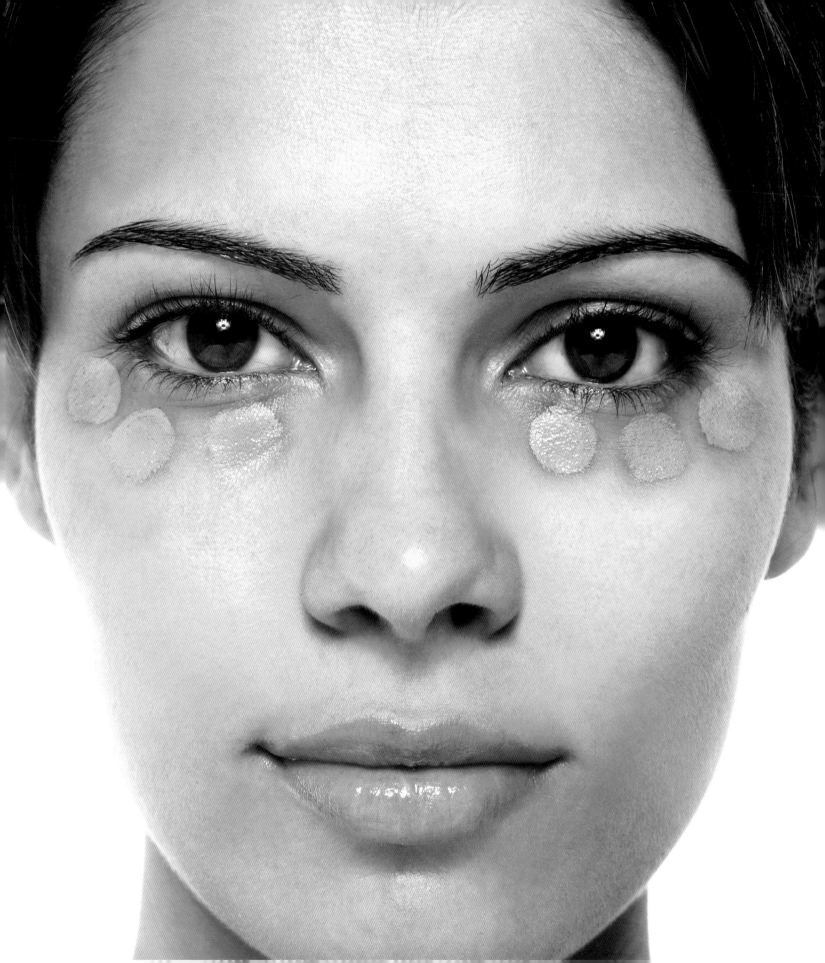

CONCEALER

Concealer is your skin's secret beauty weapon. Offering more coverage than foundation, it is ideal for disguising imperfections. There are a variety of concealer textures to choose from such as liquid, cream or stick. The trick of clever concealing is to choose and use wisely. Selecting the right colour will leave you with a flawless face, but choosing the wrong one will draw attention to the blemishes you wish to camouflage.

Here are some FAQ's answered by the experts.
How do I choose the right concealer colour?
Nina Haider: "Select a concealer that is at least one shade lighter than your skin tone. The idea is to make a darker spot or blemish blend into your complexion. Concealers vary in weight and purpose - do not assume that one concealer will meet all your needs. You will usually need two types of concealers; a fine light-reflective formula, to deal with the under-eye area and a heavier textured one to cover spots and blemishes."

Should concealer be applied before or after foundation?
Leena Jotangia: "My golden rule is to apply foundation first. A good foundation will cover the majority of spots, blemishes and redness. Only conceal those areas that need a little extra help."

Saira Hussain: "Concealer is used to disguise specific skin concerns such a sports, blemishes and dark circles. It is best to apply foundation first then fill in problem areas that are still visible with concealer. If you do it the other way round, you'll probably remove most of the concealer while blending on the foundation, making the trouble zones visible again."

What is the best way to conceal spots and blemishes?
Nina Haider: Use a cream or stick concealer that is richer in texture and provides an intense and longer lasting coverage.
1 Apply the product over the blemish using a fine-tipped brush - this will give you more precise application.
2 Blend the concealer into the skin.
3 Use a sponge to dot your foundation over the area.
4 Finish by setting the foundation using translucent powder. Remember to clean the brush regularly to avoid spreading bacteria from your skin to the concealer.

What is the best way to hide dark circles?
Nina Haider shares her secrets:
1 Start by gently patting a light eye cream under the eyes using your ring finger. This will moisturize and wake up the cells around the area. Allow the cream to settle for a minute.
2 A brush will give you the most natural coverage and more control. If like me, you prefer to use your fingers, opt for your ring finger, as it is weaker and will apply less pressure to the delicate skin around the eyes. Dab tiny dots of concealer around the orbital bone - blend and conceal using light tapping and stroking motions - until the product disappears. Avoid product overload - start with less and only build up if more coverage is needed.

In cases of severe dark circles, use a concealer formulated with orange tones. These work to cleverly highlight and neutralize discolouration without giving the under eye area a greyish appearance that lighter concealers can create.

If you are not affected by under eye circles, luckily, you won't need that extra concealer coverage and can get away with using foundation, patted lightly around the eyes. Remember that the role of concealer is to camouflage, but if you don't have anything to hide, don't use it.

CONCEALER TIPS

- Use a small concealer brush to apply and blend colour to the spot or blemish, finish off with the fingers to even out any streaks. Most experts find that the fingers are the best tools for blending around the eye area.
- Choose a yellow-based concealer, which will cancel out any under-eye discolouration. Select a creamy or liquid concealer, (both blend well into the delicate under-eye skin) with light reflecting particles that work to diminish shadows.
- Leena Jotangia: "Unless you have severe dark circles, ignore the rules on concealer such as - green covers red, yellow covers red and brown, orange covers blue. It's too fussy! Most brands have an extensive range of concealers to match almost every skin tone. These are formulated with a great deal of pigment, so a thin application will conceal or hide the various undertones. Just pick the shade that matches you best - it's simple!"

POWDER

Powder is no longer the cakey-product it used to be. Scientific advances have developed formulas that are extremely sheer in coverage and translucent in texture. Powder is a great finishing product and works as an invisible fixer to set foundation, soak up sebum and help colour cosmetics (such as blusher and eye colour) to glide on with ease without causing creasing or blotchiness.

Loose Vs. pressed powder

Powders are available in loose and pressed textures. Loose powder is designed to be applied using a brush whereas pressed powder is usually applied with a powder puff. Selecting the right application tool is vital and can make a difference to the quality of the finish.

Use a good quality powder brush to apply loose powder. A soft, voluminous brush with a fairly large head, made from natural fibre bristles, will give an amazing 'barely there' finish.

For perfect application, dip the brush in the powder and gently blow or shake off any excess from the bristles. Place the brush at the centre of the face (usually the bridge of the nose) and stroke outwards - this will ensure that the shiniest areas get the heaviest product delivery.

If you overdo your powder application, dust over the area with a clean brush to remove the excess.

Loose powder can also act as a guard for falling eye colour. Dust some powder lightly under the eyes before applying eyeshadow, and sweep it away with a soft brush once you have finished. It will prevent the face from being streaked with colour.

Pressed powder is the preferred and less messier choice for touch ups on the go. The key to perfect application is to use a powder puff to pat the product onto the skin - do not rub in the powder.

CHAPTER FIVE
EYES

EYES

The skin around the eyes is one of the first areas of the face, to show signs of ageing and frustratingly, is also the hardest area to treat. There are many reasons for this. Firstly the skin in this area is extremely thin and delicate - it is only 0.5mm thick compared to an average of 2.5mm on the rest of your body. In addition to this, the eye muscles are the most overworked part of the face. They move around 100,000 times a day, and are also affected by the daily wear and tear of make-up removal, strain through reading, harsh lighting, wind, dust, and squinting in the sun. This explains why the eyes are prone to premature ageing.

Maintaining a youthful-looking eye area can take some time, but making the effort is definitely worth it.

THE MOST COMMON PROBLEMS, THEIR CAUSES AND HOW TO TREAT THEM

Fine lines and wrinkles

Fine lines appear as we age, but can also be triggered by squinting, laughter and dryness due to dehydration around the eye area.

Regular care is essential to keep this delicate zone moisturized and revitalized.

Careful product application is important. Apply creams or gels gently around the eyes using a light, patting motion avoiding any pulling and stretching of the skin.

EYE BAGS

The following factors can trigger fluid retention, which leads to liquid waste accumulating in the under-eye tissue.

Ageing

As we age, the skin around the eye area loses its elasticity and grows thinner resulting in drooping, hooded lids and under-eye bags.

Late nights

All over puffiness usually occurs after a late night. In most cases this is a temporary problem.

Product sensitivity

Sensitivity to certain eye products, such as contact lens solutions, eye drops, make-up or skincare can trigger the problem. To avoid developing eye bags, look for products that are labeled 'fragrance free' or 'hypoallergenic'. If you notice that your eye cream is contributing to the problem, the best solution is to change brands. Eye gels are a lighter alternative to eye creams and tend to be more soothing in this area.

Diet

Food allergies and an unhealthy diet can also cause puffiness and dark circles. Cutting down on your intake of salt, caffeine and alcohol (such as red wine) can help. A healthy diet, rich in fresh fruit, vegetables and plenty of water is advised. An adequate vitamin intake, especially vitamin A can also make an improvement. Severe cases of eye bags are unlikely to disappear without having an 'eye-job', professionally known as blepharoplasty surgery. There are, however, some highly effective products on the market, as well as home remedies, that can protect the area from further damage.

Try these at home

- Place some cold cucumber slices or chilled, damp tea bags over the eye area and leave for 15 minutes.

- The chilled spoon method is also popular. Simply place two stainless steel teaspoons in the freezer. Remove from the freezer and place the bulb of the spoons over the eye area.

- Alternatively, cold sliced potatoes can be used as eye pads to reduce puffiness. If natural home solutions are not for you, refrigerated re-usable gel pads are widely available.

- Try sleeping on your back with your head elevated by an extra pillow. The angle will allow fluid to drain overnight, instead of accumulating under the eyes, which causes puffiness.

DARK CIRCLES

Dark circles can be triggered by various factors. Here are the most common.

Genetic hyperpigmentation

For some, especially amongst South Asian women, the problem is caused by genetic hyperpigmentation. Usually the circles will only become visible over time as the skin ages and loses elasticity. The skin under the eye is very thin. When blood passes through the large veins close to the surface of the skin it can produce a blue-ish tint. The more transparent your skin, the darker the circles will appear. Clever cover-up with a light-weight concealer is an easy way of hiding them. In cases of chronic dark circles, your best bet is to speak to a dermatologist who may suggest a chemical peel or laser resurfacing treatments.

Lack of sleep

Lack of sleep and excessive tiredness can contribute to dark circles. Too many late nights can lead to a pale complexion, which allows the blood underneath the skin to become darker and more visible. Catch up on your beauty sleep wherever possible and you will certainly notice a difference.

Pregnancy

Skin around the eye area can become pale during pregnancy allowing the underlying veins to become more visible.

Poor nutrition

An unbalanced diet and the lack of certain nutrients can contribute to the discolouration of this area.

Overexposure to the sun

Excessive exposure to sunlight, especially during the summer months, can cause a higher-than-normal level of skin pigmentation under the eyes even in darker skinned people.

Ageing

As we get older the skin around the eyes gets thinner, due to the gradual collapse of the 'scaffolding' formed by collagen fibres combined with the weakening of the elastic fibres that keep the skin taut. As the skin gets thinner, the blood vessels and darker shadows of bone begin to show through.

EXPERT TIP

Holistic expert, Bharti Vyas advises incorporating regular eye massage into your weekly beauty regime as a great way to guard against toxic build up. Follow these steps.

1 Close your eyes and feel the bony rims of your eye sockets.

2 Starting at the outer edge, use your ring fingers to trace around the rims of the sockets, applying more pressure across your brow and at the point where the eyebrow meets the side of the nose.

3 Do at least ten 'laps' at a steady pace, working on both eyes simultaneously.

EYEBROWS

Eyebrows are one of our most important facial assets - they frame the eyes, structure the proportion of the face and give it an identity. A well-shaped brow can lift and open the eyes, helping us look younger and well groomed. Some brow experts believe that a perfectly shaped pair can have the same effect as a mini face-lift.

Change your brow shape and you can instantly re-define your features. Be it thick or thin, brow shapes change constantly with fashion. Whether you opt for the au naturel look like Kajol or the high-maintenance, Aishwarya-esque perfectly arched brow - the choice of shape and method of creating it is entirely up to you!

EYEBROW SHAPING METHODS

Threading

Threading is a practice that is familiar to most of us and is the preferred method for the majority of women in the subcontinent. It's completely hygienic, quick and a relatively pain free method of hair removal. It involves shaping of the brows using a cotton thread. The thread is twisted and rolled along the surface of the skin intertwining with hairs, which removes them from the follicle. This method gives a neat and precise finish and lasts for approximately two-three weeks. Threading can also be used to remove hair from other areas of the face such as the upper lip and chin.

Waxing

This method is best left to the professionals, as it can be tricky to get it right yourself. Brow-waxing is similar to waxing your legs, but involves higher concentration, as the shape needs to be carefully groomed. The therapist spreads a thin layer of wax over the area, a hair removal cloth is pressed over it and quickly pulled away, taking the stray hairs with it.

Plucking

Plucking is the easiest and most common method of shaping the brows and removing re-growth between threading and waxing. Even if you don't choose to shape your entire brow with a tweezer, they will always come in handy when you need to pluck out those unruly strays.

Electrolysis

Electrolysis is a costly but permanent way of obtaining your desired shape. The good thing is that you don't have to worry about re-growth, as the hairs will never grow back, but it limits your future choices as you're stuck with the same shape.

HANDY BROW TIPS

- When choosing the right brow shape consider factors such as age, lifestyle and natural shape. It is imperative that you don't go against your natural shape - the idea is to enhance it.

- "Thicker eyebrows give your face a younger appearance and look great on women under 35 years of age. After this time I advise my clients to go for thinner brows", says brow expert, Shavata Singh.

- If you decide to have your brows professionally shaped and do not know where to go, always ask someone whose eyebrows are well groomed. Check the brows of your potential therapist - this is always a good indication of how good they are.

- The shape of your eyes will determine the eyebrow shape that will suit your face. So go with it and don't try to copy someone else's shape as it may not suit you. A general rule is - the highest part of your brow bone is where the brow should arch and from this point it should gradually slope down.

- Use a transparent brow gel or lash comb to brush the brows upwards and outwards into shape. This will give you a lady-like refined finish.

PLUCKING PERFECTION

If you dare not part with your tweezers - here are some handy hints from eyebrow specialist Shavata.

"A professionally manicured eyebrow can truly make a difference. Everyone should get their brows professionally shaped, even if it is only once a year. It will give you an idea of what they should look like, and with regular maintenance they can remain perfectly shaped. Once you have the brows you love, tend to them on a daily basis; it's a lot easier to tweeze one or two stray hairs every day then a bunch at the end of the week."

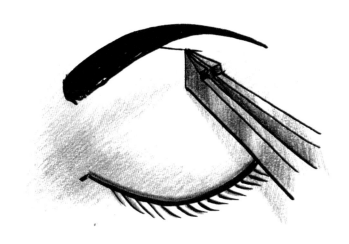

When shaping your own brows there are a few rules to follow:

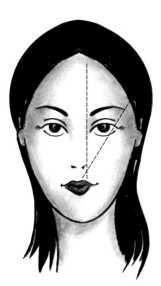

Eyebrows should start before the eye (nose side) and not after. To find the start and end point, hold a pencil at the side of the tip of the nose. This is where the brow should start. Move the pencil to the outer corner of the eye (where the eye ends) and this is where the brow should finish.

Try to keep the shape even and avoid leaving a thick chunk of hair at the inner edge of the brows. There is nothing worse than a tadpole-shaped brow framing the eyes.

When shaping the brows always pluck after a hot shower, in natural daylight.

When tweezing, sit in front of a large mirror with a second, magnified mirror in your hand. This gives you an overall view and the hand mirror helps with the detail.

No two eyebrows are ever identical; so do not attempt to get them to the same shape, as you will end up plucking to nothing. Eyebrows are sisters not twins.

Always pluck both brows simultaneously. Pluck three or four hairs from one brow then repeat on the other side. It is easier and much better to do this, rather than do a whole brow and then the other. Trying to mimic one brow shape after the other is very difficult.

Be sure to tweeze in the direction that the hair grows and pluck only one hair at a time. The more you pluck, the slower the re-growth will be. It takes 56 days for the hair fiber to regenerate and as long as the follicle has not been damaged, the hair will grow back as before. So be careful not to over-pluck and harm the follicle.

Brow shading and filling tips

"When applying make up to the brows less is always more. You should never be able to see where the make-up starts and where the hairs stop. When holding the brow pencil always hold further down - like you would when sketching, and gradually build up the colour."
Aysha

"When filling in the brow, always keep the brow pencil one shade lighter than your hair colour, this will give a more natural result." **Nina Haider**

Which tweezers?

Slanted tweezers are preferred by models and make-up artists, as they are better at gripping obstinate hairs. Pointy tweezers are precise and are great if you can get the hang of using them.

64

EYELASHES

Every woman yearns for a great set of lashes and advancements in cosmetics means you can enhance them in any way you please. Whether you want to add curl, length, volume, or change their colour, there are countless amounts of products and treatments out there that are designed to meet your lash needs.

Mascara

In days gone by women would use burnt matchsticks to darken their eyelashes. Fortunately, today we do not have to go to such extremes. The invention of mascara means we can all have fluttery lashes in a sweep of a wand.

Some make-up artists say that the actual mascara brush is more important than the formulation. So what shape of brush should you go for?

A slightly rigid brush, with well spaced bristle allow for thicker application - great for those of you who want to add volume.

A long, cylindrical brush with tight bristles is best for lengthening and making the lashes look longer.

Curved wands are perfect for curling the lashes.

How to apply mascara

You may think this is too simple to need a detailed step by step explanation, but you will be surprised by the amount of ladies who get it wrong. Too many women have overly-spiked or clumpy-looking lashes, and nothing can be blamed apart from clumsy application.

Here are a few pointers on how to get it right every time.

• For a wide-eyed look, curl the upper lashes with an eyelash curler before applying mascara.

• Coat lashes from the root up to the tips by wiggling the brush back and forth, it's a great way of making them look fuller. It's important that the lash base be coated as close to the eyelid as possible. This defines the eye shape and keeps the application looking natural.

• Separate the lashes by combing them with a lash comb. It is easier to separate them before they have dried.

• Hold the brush parallel to the nose and coat the bottom lashes with the tip of the brush.

• Avoid colour smudging on the skin as you apply it to your lower lashes. Place a mirror flat on a table in front of you and look down as you apply the mascara. This will increase the space between the lashes and the skin allowing you to brush more freely.

MASCARA TIPS

• If your mascara is clumpy wipe the wand off with a tissue before application.

• Always remove your mascara at night. If you leave it on out of laziness, not only will you wake to a nasty smear, but it will also dry the lashes causing the follicles to clog while you sleep.

• Replace your mascara every three months. Old mascara is the breeding ground for germs.

• Avoid pumping the mascara wand in and out of the tube in an aim to give it an even coverage. This only traps air inside the tube and dries it out.

• Correct mascara mishaps on the skin by dipping a cotton-bud into your eye make-up remover and gently blending away the mistake.

CURLING YOUR LASHES

Curling the lashes can give you a wide-eyed look almost instantaneously. Used properly (which can take some getting used to), the eyelash curler can give the lashes instant life and even double their length.

Spending a little extra on a good-quality curler is worth the investment, as these usually come with non-stick silicone pads, which are gentler on the lashes compared to the cheaper options.

Always remember to clean the curler pads with a cotton-bud and get a new one as soon as the rubber starts to crack.

Curl lashes prior to mascara application, but you can also do it the other way round. The trick is to allow the mascara to dry for five minutes so that lashes don't stick to the curler.

FALSE LASHES

Fake lashes are great for adding length and volume to your natural lashes and are a lot easier to apply than you may think. There are two types of false lashes and each creates a different effect. Full lashes are thicker and can be used to give density to the entire lash line - great for adding a touch of drama on an evening out. Individual lashes look more subtle and are ideal for filling in sparse areas or for creating a fluttery-eyed look.

Application Tips
Full fake lashes

Once you get the hang of it, false lashes are not that difficult to apply - all you need is a little patience and a steady hand. Here's how it's done.

Make-up artists suggest drawing a smoky line of colour either with a pencil or thin liner brush; this will conceal the 'obvious' look of the false lash line.

Curl your own lashes before applying the false ones, this will help to disguise the glue and hold the false lashes in place.

Individual fake lashes

Individual lashes are sold in different lengths and colours and are available in either a cluster or as a single lash. They look more natural when the different sizes are mixed together. Application of individual lashes require a steady hand and a little more patience.

Follow these tips

1 Grip the lash between a pair of tweezers and dip it in some eyelash glue.
2 Apply the lash at the outer corner of the lash line and hold down until secure.

1 Place a drop of eyelash glue on the back of your hand (wait 30 seconds for the glue to become sticky), drag the base of the lash through the glue or use the tip from the back of a brush to tap the glue on.

2 Apply the lash as close to the natural lash line as possible. Start at the outer corner of the eye and work inwards using light pressure until the band is fixed.

3 To secure, tap the lash line with the handle of a small brush. Curl again, and add a second coat of mascara.

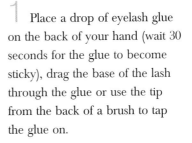

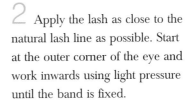

Other lash-enhancing options

Lash extensions is a fairly new innovation and involves bonding individual, single false (synthetic) lashes onto your own. The procedure is painless, but delicate. It results in fuller, longer and natural-looking lashes that can last for up to three months.

Lash perms involve small rods being placed on the lashes and when removed, they leave you with temporarily curled lashes - a great option for those of you who do not have the time to curl daily. Results can last up to 12 weeks.

Anjana's Top Tip!

It's best to keep this look for special occasions as fake lashes can feel heavy on the lids and long-term use may lead to eye irritation. Always use the rubber type glue that is provided with the lashes. Remove the lashes with light tugging - it's pain free once you get the hang of it.

EYESHADOW

Most of us will agree that eyeshadow is the one make-up skill we have yet to fully master. Getting the skill of eye make-up right can take time and patience.

"The eyes are the most important and balancing feature of the face. It is very easy to get eye make-up completely wrong. Just remember, most of the time, less is definitely more. Sometimes just a light wash of a bright colour teamed with lashings of mascara can enhance the entire eye area," says make-up artist Kapil Bhalla.

COLOUR

Coloured eyeshadows are no longer the basic-matte formulas worn by our grandmothers. Thankfully, beauty houses have done all they can to increase our choice, with the creation of textures and pigments that are diverse and fashionable.

Coloured eyeshadows can help you make a statement or add a touch of drama on a night out. A strong, solid colour on the eyelids, can work just as well as a rainbow of different shades blended together. The trick is to choose your shade well, because doing so, can make your eyes sparkle. The wrong colour can do the opposite, making the eyes look dull and lifeless.

When it comes to colour selection, there are no set rules, so do not be frightened. It is fun to experiment and play around with different hues and textures, it's the only way you will find what works for you.

EXPERT TIPS ON COLOUR

"Mix and match colour for a younger feel or stick to earthy tones for a more classic finish. If you feel comfortable then go with it." **Mehera Khola**

"Eyeshadow colour does not necessarily have to match your outfit - matching colour can look dated. Clashing colours can give eyes a modern finish."
Kapil Bhalla

"Head to your favourite cosmetic counter and have your eyes made up by a pro. Ask for colour combinations that could work for both day and evening." **Leena Jotangia**

"Stick to shades in the same family of colours - it is always more flattering on the eye." **Clint Fernandes**

"Eyeshadow can look a lot more vibrant in its packaging, so don't let colour intensity keep you from trying a shade you like. What looks bright in its packaging can look more subtle on the skin." **Naveeda**

"I personally don't think South Asian women should avoid any eyeshadow colours. Just apply bright shades moderately." **Clint Fernandes**

"If you have deep set eyes, avoid using dark colours on the inner corners of the lids. This can make the eyes look even deeper. Opt for lighter colours instead."
Pooja Arora

"Metallic eye colour gives more depth and intensity to evening eye make-up. A smudged and blended black kohl liner pencil applied on the eyelid and then blended over with a purple metallic shadow can look striking, as can a turquoise or green. Blending well, however, is the key to successful make-up, always."
Cory Wallia

COLOUR CHOICE FOR YOUR COMPLEXION

Fair skin
Cory Wallia: "There are a number of colours that work well on fair skin tone, including turquoise, aqua, lilac, pink and some shades of oranges, lime green, olive and khaki."

Clint Fernandes: "Although these colours look great - go easy on the application as overdoing it can look tacky."

Aysha: "For daily wear go for a warmer colour palette with neutral shades such a warm brown, beige, and soft silver. Even metallic textures in pastel shades can create an eye-catching finish. Avoid strong colours, which can look too harsh for this skin tone."

Medium skin tone
Cory Wallia: "Choose colours that are warm and slightly deeper in tone. Lilacs and mauves can look striking."

Aysha: "Bright shades of blue, purple, pink and green can look striking against this skin tone. If you prefer a more muted colour palette, opt for metallic copper, gold and bronze, tones."

Dusky skin
Cory Wallia: "Dusky beauties can carry almost any shade. Use all the colours a fair complexion can carry but make sure that these colours are deeper in intensity."

Clint Fernandes: "Smoky eyes or warm metallic tones of copper, gold and bronze can look fabulous."

Aysha: "When it come to colour choice, you can be a lot more versatile with darker complexions as this skin tone can carry an array of shades. Smoky eyes using hues of black, navy or charcoal can look smouldering. Different shades from the gold colour family, such as bronze and cinnamon can create a sun-kissed effect. The more daring can play around with vivid colours such as bright pink and green."

GET THE LOOK: Colourful Eyes by Mehera Khola

1 Prime the lids by smoothing some foundation over them. This will create an even base for colour application and give the eyeshadow something to cling to.

2 Use a brush to lightly sweep some translucent powder over the eyelids.

3 Dust plenty of loose powder under the lower lashes - this will act as a guard to catch any flecks of falling colour pigment. Sweep away at the end.

4 When it comes to colour application, the basic rule is, less is more. Always start application with very little colour, you can always blend and add more to build up the intensity if needed. After deciding on the desired effect, apply eye colour with an eyeshadow brush. If you are using more than one colour, remember to blend well. This will ensure that no hard lines or separation between colours are visible. Make sure that colour fades outwards towards the outer edges of the lids. Do not allow it to crease - just blend, blend, blend! To make shimmery or metallic colours look more intense, apply using a wet brush. Avoid smudging by making sure you keep the eyes closed until the lids feel dry.

5 Complete the desired look by grooming the brows with a brow brush, curling the lashes and coating them with mascara.

EYESHADOW TEXTURES

Understanding eyeshadow texture can make application simpler. Here are the different types.

Powder shadows are best applied with a brush. They have excellent staying power, which makes them the preferred texture for evening looks. High-quality pressed eyeshadows, (which are usually more expensive) contain strong pigments, making colour exposure visible on the first stroke.

Cream shadows have a lightweight and almost skin-like texture. They glide onto the lids with ease and can be applied and blended using the fingers. This texture is a great option for speedy eye make-up and for those of you who do not feel confident enough to play around with brushes.

Gel shadows are packaged in a similar way to cream shadows. Colour pigments are compressed into a gel formulation. It can be applied with ease and leaves behind a long lasting finish.

Eyeshadow crayons are shaped like thick pencils. Colour is applied by literally drawing directly onto the eyelids. They are easy to apply and can be blended by using the fingertips.

Multi-purpose products are available in push-up or roll-up type sticks. Use them for colour application on the eyes, lips or cheeks. They are creamy in texture and need to be blended well with the fingertips - a must have for quick touch-ups on the go.

Loose pigment or glitter eyeshadows are high sheen products that can be used to add some extra jazz to the eyes - giving an instant effect of glamour. They are often used by make-up artists at fashion shows and photoshoots. These products are difficult to press into a compact form so you will usually find them packed loosely into small pots. The best way to apply loose powder, shimmer or glitter is with a brush. Dampening your make-up brush can make application slightly easier and give you longer lasting coverage.

74

GET THE LOOK

10-Minute Eyes by Kapil Bhalla

For a natural no make-up look follow these steps.

1 Add a touch of deep, matte brown eyeshadow to the socket area to create some depth.

2 Use an eyelash curler to curl the lashes.

3 Add some hair gel to a clear mascara wand and groom the eyebrows in place - you are ready to go!

Catwalk Eyes by Cory Wallia

Get high-drama catwalk eyes, which work amazingly when you want that supermodel-look for a glam evening out.

1 Prepare the eyelids with foundation and powder. Pat some loose powder under the lower lashes, which should be removed after colour application

2 Use a black pencil liner to mark the upper lash line. Gently smudge the liner using an eyeshadow brush.

3 Apply some silvery or frosty eyeshadow onto the lids blending well with the smudged liner using upward and outward strokes.

4 Apply a kohl liner on the inner, upper and lower rims of the eyes. This will give eyes a dramatic but sexy edge.

5 To finish, curl the lashes then carefully apply plenty of mascara, creeping the wand gently up the lashes to extend them as far as possible. Use a frosty highlighter under the arch of the brows. It looks gorgeous and gives you an instant catwalk look. A thin line of glitter gel applied over a thicker black eyeliner on the top lid also gives superb catwalk effects.

Anjana's Top Tip!
The secret to model-like flirty lashes is to fake it. We use fake lashes at almost every fashion show and photoshoot - they instantly open up the eyes.

Shimmery Eyes by Kapil Bhalla

Iridescent or metallic eyeshadows are great for adding some bling to the eyes on a big night out. This look works beautifully with a dewy base and creamy cheeks.

1 Sweep foundation over the lids and set with powder. Groom the eyebrows into place with a brow comb.

2 Using a brush, apply a loose iridescent powder eyeshadow, (in a colour of your choice) over the entire eyelid.

3 Dab on a touch of clear lip-gloss to the centre of the lids as well as on the brow bone.

4 Using your fingertips, gently press on some fine silver glitter, ensuring the entire lid has an even application. Dust off any excess that has fallen with a large powder brush.

5 Finish by applying a generous coat of black mascara to the upper and lower lashes.

Glossy Eyes by Clint Fernandes

Clint says, "Be warned, this look is high-maintenance and high-fashion. I wouldn't recommended it for daily wear and this is a look that is ideally more flattering for the young."

1 Prepare the eyes with foundation. Keep the coverage light - to avoid caking between the creases.

2 Pat some loose powder under the lower lashes. This will act as a magnet to falling colour pigments and can be swept away with a large brush after application.

3 Use a single eyeshadow colour as a base shade. For a natural look, go for a neutral flesh tone or pick a vibrant colour for a high-glam effect. Using an eyeshadow brush, sweep your chosen colour evenly over the lids and up to the brow bone.

4 Curl the lashes and apply mascara.

5 Using a brush, gently and evenly dab some Vaseline over the entire lid for a glossy finish.

EYESHADOW TIPS

• Always dab on some foundation on the eyelids and powder gently to create a smooth base for the eyeshadow to sit.

• Tweeze, pluck and groom eyebrows. Tidy brows will instantly enhance eye make-up.

• Mature skin with visible fine lines tends to look best with matte eyeshadow and smoky, smudged eyeliner.

• You can mix eyeshadows of different textures, but always use powdery textures for highlighting or shading on top of a creamy base colour (never the other way round).

• Use pearly, shimmering eyeshadow in pale or frosty colours on the brow bone. Add a dab to the centre of the eyelid for an instant wide-eyed look.

• It is a good idea to use brushes of different sizes for different purposes. Blend the base colour with the largest brush. Highlight using a medium-sized brush and use the smallest brush to apply dark shades to the crease of the lids.

Anjana's Top Tip!
On special occasions use some eye drops before applying your eye make-up. This instantly whitens the whites and adds sparkle.

GET THE LOOK
Smoky Eyes by Mickey Contractor

The smoky eye look is an all time classic. It's smouldering, sexy and always in fashion.
It gives the eyes a touch of mystery and looks fabulous in softer evening light.

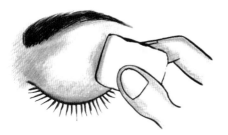

1 Prepare the lids for make-up. Use a small sponge to apply a thin layer of foundation to the entire eyelid - this creates a great base for colour to rest. Sweep some translucent loose powder across the top of the cheekbone, just under the eyes. This will catch any falling eyeshadow particles, which can be easily swept away.

2 Use a flat eyeshadow brush or sponge-tipped applicator to apply a mid-toned colour over the entire eyelid. Blend the colour at the outer edge of the eyelid to soften.

3 Next, take a darker eyeshadow in a similar colour and apply to the lids - starting at the outer corner of the eye and blending inwards almost up to the middle of the lid. Make sure you blend well - the colour difference of the two shadows should not be visible - the idea is to make it look like one colour, only varying in intensity.

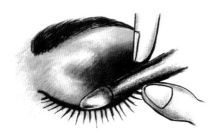

4 Use a cream, liquid or pencil liner to trace along the upper lash line. Lightly, blend and smudge the liner into the eyeshadow using a small shadow brush. This is what will give the eyes a 'smoky' definition.

5 Apply a kohl pencil to the upper and lower inner rims of the eyes, in a colour that compliments the rest of the eye make-up.

6 Using a fine-tipped brush, apply the same shade used on the upper eyelids to line the area under the lower lashes. Use as little colour as possible and remember to blend outwards to avoid a harsh line. Brush some highlighter on the brow bone (this is optional). I like to use a colour that is pretty discreet and my favourite is MAC eyeshadow in Ricepaper. Finally, curl the lashes and lay on the mascara, thickly. The best way to compliment a smoky eye is by using a light shade of lip-colour.

KOHL

Our eyes are one of our most alluring features and kohl is the perfect accessory to accentuate them. A stroke of kohl instantly draws attention to the eyes by adding definition. The different colour options means it is versatile enough to be applied lightly for a daytime look or intensley for an evening look.

The use of kohl on the eyes of both men and women is thought to have originated in ancient Egypt. Egyptian women would generously apply it around their eyes, sometimes extending it outwards at the corners. This ritual was reserved for depictions of royalty or gods. Look at any picture of Queen Cleopatra - and immediately, you are drawn to her elaborately kohl-defined eyes.

Traditionally, women across South Asia would make it in their homes using the soot from an oil lamp, which when mixed with pure castor oil would produce pure kajal. The castor oil gave an incredible cooling effect to the eyes. Kohl powder was either applied with the fingers or with a beautiful stick applicator, usually made of wood, bone, silver or ivory. The applicator would be moistened with water, rosewater or olive oil before being dipped into a kohl pot and applied to the eyes.

Thankfully, nowadays the application method is a lot more practical and the invention of the kohl pencil is a godsend. Most Indian women would consider it as the one cosmetic item they can't do without. No matter how often fashion changes the kohl liner will always remain in vogue.

How to apply kohl by Aysha

1 To apply kohl to the inside of the eye, gently pull down the lower eyelid rim, start at the inner corner and draw a line using gentle strokes of the pencil.

2 For a dramatic evening look, try lining the inside upper rims.

Anjana's Top Tip!
If you fancy a change from the black kohl liner, use brown for a subtle daytime look. It works in the same way but gives a more youthful finish by taking away the harshness that black can sometimes give.

Did you know?

- It may surprise you to know that enhancing one's features was not always the only reason for wearing kohl. Across South Asia it was worn by men, women and children as protection against eye ailments, diseases and inflammation.
  Even now, from the time a child is six days old, some mothers will apply a small black dot on the chin or behind the ear to ward of evil. Some women of all ages still practice this tradition to protect themselves from envious eyes.

- In Egypt, kohl powder was kept in shells. Then in small handmade containers made of ivory, alabaster, porcelain, glass, silver, or wood. It is still possible to find ornate silver kohl containers known as "makhallas".

- The Ancient Egyptians must have discovered that the whites of the eyes appeared whiter after using kohl, which creates a striking effect when combined with dark eye colour.

- In South Asia, kohl has many other names, including Kajal, Al-kahl, Surma and Anjur.

BOLLYWOOD AND KOHL

In the film Jism, Bipasha Basu's iconic look for the character Sonia was created by make-up guru Kapil Bhalla - he shares the story behind the look.

"Jism was a make-up artist's dream and the film is still known and will be remembered for Bipasha and her sexy look. The day Pooja Bhatt briefed me about the make-up look for Jism, I was already envisioning the blackest of black kohl pencils, charcoal eyeliners and smouldering grey eyeshadows. The entire colour palette of her look revolved around smudged, smoky greys with the deepest black kohl liner. Her character had to look unbelievably beautiful and she did!"

"The most exciting part was her introduction in the film where she walks out of the sea-waters with deep charcoal bird-like eyes. Bipasha cannot do without a black kohl pencil and throughout the film, I keep the signature kohl eyes and we named the look 'bird-eye'."

GET THE 'BIRD-EYE' LOOK

1 Prep the eyelid with foundation and dust some translucent powder under the lower lashes. This can be removed once the look is complete.

2 Using a shadow brush - sweep a dull gold eyeshadow over the eyelids, always blending outwards.

3 Line the inner, upper and lower rims of the eyes with a black kohl pencil (my favourite is Smoulder by MAC).

4 Line the upper lash line using the same pencil. Smudge the liner using a brush and a touch of a black powder eyeshadow.

5 Carefully draw peaks at the inner and outer corner of the eye using a sharpened black liner pencil. The key here is to extend the liner all the way at the top and bottom. To sharpen the finish - trace over it with a liquid or cream eyeliner.

6 Complete the look with lots of mascara and, for the authentic Bipasha look, add some individual false lashes to the outer corners of the lids.

7 Keep the rest of your make-up minimal - apply a deep coral colour to the cheeks with a light dusting of shimmering bronzer. Keep the lips pale and glossy.

LIQUID LINER

Eyeliners are the most extensively used form of eye make-up. Used correctly, they can make the eyes appear more prominent and create an illusion of thicker lashes. Liquid liners can appear quite harsh compared to pencil liners, which give a softer and subtler finish. Mastering the application technique may take some getting used to, but practice makes perfect.

How to apply liquid eyeliner by Pooja Arora

1 The right tool is essential for achieving the heavily-lined look. Use a pointy liner brush that will allow you to draw a clean and precise line. We've all made the mistake of closing our eyes when applying liner and this often leads to a messy finish. The trick is to keep the eye slightly open - which makes it easier to follow the contour of the lash-line.

2 Before application, stroke the brush against the mouth of the liner tube to remove excess liquid and taper the brush to a fine point.

3 Look into the mirror and tilt your head back slightly, keeping your eyes half-open. Using the tip of the brush, line the lids. Begin at the inner corner of the lid and continue to the outer corner. Apply the liner evenly using short brush strokes. Remember to keep the liner as close to the base of the lashes as possible.

4 Let the liner dry before opening your eyes fully.

EXPERT TIPS

Kapil Bhalla: Extended eyeliner looks great, but remember to gently lift the eyelid just before extending it.

Nina Haider: When using liner don't feel like you have to paint one continuous line. Try this easy technique; Draw three dashes on the lids - one at the inner corner, one in the middle of the lash line and another at the outer corner. Then, go back and connect them.

Mickey Contractor: To soften the look of harsh eyeliner, smudge it a little using a brush.

Saira Hussain: If you find it really difficult to achieve a straight line, apply a kohl pencil before using the liquid liner, but make sure you sharpen the pencil first. Don't forget to wait for your liquid liner to dry before you rush out of the house. The last thing you want is liner stains on the crease of your eyelids-which is not very attractive.

Aysha: If you have small eyelids, avoid applying the liner thickly on the upper lashline. It will only make the eyes appear smaller.

Ruby Hammer: Liquid liner always looks more dramatic and therefore is better for a night-time look. Use a brush applicator and apply one sweep along the upper lash line with a slight kick at the end. Don't be afraid of making mistakes - you can clean up the line afterwards with a cotton-bud if necessary.

CHAPTER SIX
CHEEKS

CHEEKS

Blusher is a make-up bag basic. Applying the correct texture and shade of cheek colour in the right areas can enhance the skin's natural glow and give the complexion a healthy looking flush. Make the mistake of applying the wrong colour, in the wrong areas and you could end up looking like a circus clown. Many women find blush difficult to apply and some of you may even be confused when it comes to choosing the right shade - both factors are enough to put you off altogether. The fear of looking 'clown-like' can be a scary thought. But once you have got the colour right and mastered the art of application, blusher can transform your complexion within seconds. Blusher adds warmth to the face, emphasizes the facial contours and gives the skin a youthful looking glow.

COLOUR OPTIONS

The huge choice of colour and textures options can make selection even harder. Most make-up artists tend to agree that for a natural finish choose the colour your cheeks turn after you have pinched them or just after you have been exercising. Cheek colour should look natural and blend with your skin tone. The key is not to go too light or too dark. If you have a fair to medium complexion, opt for rosy, pink or coral tones. A duskier skin tone comes to life with copper, warm almond and deep bronze shades.

Make-up artist Ruby Hammer says: "South Asian skin tones can vary from pale to very dusky so you will need to find a shade to compliment your complexion. The general rule is that the darker the complexion the more vibrant and intense the colour can be. The other factor to take into account is the outfit you are wearing. If this is rich in colour, as some traditional dresses can be, then stick to the same tones - for example a pink outfit will look wrong with an orange blusher but great with a shade of pink that suits your complexion."

TEXTURE OPTIONS

Powder blusher is available in a plethora of colours and is the most popular choice as they are easy to blend and control. Apply on top of your foundation and under powder using a good quality brush. They are especially good for oily skin types.

Cream blusher is easy to apply. It glides onto the skin with ease and unlike powder, can give a more natural daytime finish. Apply cream blusher after foundation, but before powder. Tap on a small amount to the cheeks and blend immediately to avoid streaking. Blend upwards and outwards in a circular motion, ensuring you keep within the apple of the cheek (the apple is the part of the cheeks that raises when you smile). Its creamy texture makes it an ideal option for dry or mature skin.

Gel blusher offers the sheerest of finishes and is great for giving the cheeks a natural-looking glow. Its smooth texture makes it easy to apply, ideally over moisturizer or foundation and is a great option for the summer. Its colour pigments are very strong, so wash your hands after application. The last thing you want to do, is walk around with rose-tipped fingers!

Liquid blusher gives the cheeks a flushed, youthful and long lasting finish. Be sure to blend as soon as you apply to the skin so as not to stain and remember to wash your fingers afterwards.

Highlighting lotions and sticks come in either solid or liquid textures and are available in an array of shades. Highlighters are mainly used to accentuate the cheek and brow bones, but can also be used over the shoulder blades and décolletage for a subtle sheen.

Shimmer or glitter powders look particularly effective when applied to the cheek and brow bones. They leave behind a shimmery finish, which looks great on nights out.

Anjana's Top Tip!
I always carry my NARS Multiple highlighter (the original all-in-one make-up stick) in my handbag. My favourite shade is Copacabana. It's the ultimate multi-purpose product which can be used on any part of the face to add colour on the go!

BLUSHER APPLICATION TIPS

Knowing exactly where to apply blusher can be tricky, but understanding the shape of your face will help you to get it right. Follow these tips and discover how to use cheek colour in a way that flatters your bone structure.

The apple technique

This is the easiest and most flattering application technique to use to enhance your features - and it works on all face shapes. It gives skin the most natural looking application and always looks good.

How to do the apple technique

1 Look into the mirror and smile. The raised part of the cheek is called the "apple" and is the starting point and most flattering area on which to apply colour.

If you are using powder blush, take your blusher brush, dip into the product and gently blow or shake off any excess powder. Sweep the colour onto the apple using small, circular motions. Only build up the colour intensity if you feel you need to.
Blend well until you have just a hint of natural looking colour. You want a wash of colour rather than an obvious line.

2 Relax your smile and move the brush up and down to ensure an even and natural looking application that fades out well.

3 Cream, gel and liquid blushers should be applied in the same way but ensure you start with little colour and gradually build on it if necessary. Blending well is vital for a natural finish.

Anjana's Top Tip!

Unlike eye and lip make-up which will change with seasonal trends, once you get your blusher right, you can stick with the same shade forever.

How to do the sophisticated blush technique

This method is great for adding definition to the cheek area and ideal for those of you with prominent cheekbones.

1 Dip a smaller sized blusher brush into the powder and blow off any excess.
2 Start at the point just below the middle of the cheek. Apply the colour underneath and directly onto the cheekbones. Extend the blusher upwards and outwards towards the hairline, making sure you add a tiny touch of colour along the temples.
3 Dab a little highlighter to the cheekbones to accentuate them further.

EXPERT TIPS

"Always use a professional blusher brush - they can be expensive, but last for years and are well worth the investment." **Naveeda**

"Whatever blush texture you use, one basic rule always applies - start with little colour and gradually build up. Overdoing blusher can have disastrous results so moderation is essential." **Kapil Bhalla**

"After applying cheek colour, finish off the look with a light, shimmery, translucent powder. This will maintain the look without compromising on the glow." **Aysha**

"If you've been a little too heavy handed with the powder blush you can tone down the colour by blending in a little face powder. To minimize cream blush, simply blot the colour using a tissue. Gel and liquid blush can stain the cheeks and the only way to lighten them is it to wash it off with water." **Nina Haider**

"For longer lasting blusher, smooth on a little cream blush and then apply a powder blush in the same colour family. Using two different textures will ensure it stays put." **Pooja Arora**

BRONZER

We all love that golden glow a bit of sun-worshipping can give us. A tan can light up the skin and gives an appealing hue to the face and body. Bronzers achieve a similar affect to tanning, but are the smarter and healthier way of adding a sun-kissed glow. Use it to achieve that year round 'just been on holiday look' without actually having to sacrifice your skin to the sun's harmful rays.

Bronzers are probably the least purchased item by those with dusky skin tones, mainly because of the name, which suggests a darkening-effect. But, don't let the name frighten you or assume it will make your skin look darker. Careful selection of the right shade can give skin a beautiful glow that can't be achieved with blusher. Give it a go and you'll be surprised by the results.

How to choose a bronzer

When choosing a bronzer never go more than two shades darker than your natural skin tone. Its job is to add warmth to the skin, not colour it.

Powder bronzers are ideal for oily complexions. For a more dewy-looking finish opt for a cream or gel texture.

Make-up artist Aysha says: "You should go for a colour that is a little darker than your natural skin tone and opt for warmer hues rather than one that is too red. MAC do fantastic bronzers, my favourite is 'Golden' for lighter skin tones and 'Bronze' for medium toned skin."

Anjana's Top Tip!
Give your skin a 'beach babe' glow by mixing a touch of liquid bronzer with your foundation. It adds a wonderful glisten.

BRONZER APPLICATION TIPS

• It is important to use the correct brush. Choose one that is wide and fluffy. Dip the brush into the colour and tap it on the back of your hand to remove any excess. Apply colour to the areas of the face that the sun would naturally hit, such as the cheeks, forehead, chin and bridge of the nose. Make sure you blend well to avoid streaking and patching.

• Cream, stick and liquid bronzers should be applied using the fingers and blended in well to avoid streaking. Don't forget to dab colour on the bridge of the nose, chin and a touch on the forehead to add warmth and bring the features together.

• "As with blushers - stick to the rule of starting light and gradually building up the colour," says Naveeda. "The trick is not to overload the brush. If you apply too much you can end up looking an unattractive shade of orange. The whole point of bronzer is to give the skin a sun-kissed glow and minimum application always works best."

• When using bronzer, try to keep the rest of your make-up simple. A few coats of mascara, with a deep brown or black kohl liner teamed up with sheer or glossy lips in a shade of coral or rust will look simply stunning.

• To finish off an evening look apply some bronzer along the shoulder blades to add instant sheen. Strategically dusted bronzer dabbed between the breasts can make the cleavage stand out.

CHAPTER SEVEN
LIPS

LIPS

The lips are one of the most prominent and captivating features on the face. We communicate through our mouth and therefore draw constant attention to this area.

Full rounded lips are considered the most sensual and intriguing, but some women are happier with a thinner pout. Whatever the shape or size, with the help of cosmetics such as lipsticks, liners, plumpers and cosmetic fillers, we are able to achieve the lip shape we desire.

There was a time when lipstick was the single most iconic item in every woman's make-up bag. With continuous advancements in textures and shades it's not surprising the it still remains a must-have beauty accessory for every season.

The new breed of lip colours come in a variety of formulations from matte to sheer to glossy finishes. Added ingredients can give you further options that are long lasting, plumping or moisturising. Some even include SPF.

LIP COLOUR

Applying the right shade of lipstick can instantly give you a confidence boost and an immediate feeling of being dressed up. Some women even admit to feeling naked without a bit of colour on their lips. Many of us spend hours at cosmetic counters hunting for that perfect colour. Finding the right shade can take some time, but once you find your colour it can brighten up the face and give you an instant high.

Your skin tone will help determine the colours that will work with your complexion. When it comes to South Asian skin tones there are a few guidelines that need to be followed, to lead you to the right colour choice. Being colour-savvy is essential - buying a lipstick, just because you like the colour, is a complete no-no. Remember, the lipstick needs to compliment your skin tone and enhance your colouring. The right hue can make skin look beautiful but the wrong one can make you look ill.

COLOUR CHOICE TIPS
Colour options are so broad that you can't be blamed for being confused. These guidelines from Clint Fernandes will help you find the perfect match.

Fair complexions can carry off most lip shades. Depending on the eye make-up and event you could use almost any colour; however, dark plums and maroons can look a little gothic.

Olive and mid-tone complexions look good in shades with warm undertones, which can instantly brighten up the skin. Avoid bright pinks and certain shades of red. If you like deeper lip colour opt for browner reds such as berry or wine.

Dusky complexions should avoid use of bright colours or shades that are too light (such as flesh tones). Bronzes and golds can look stunning, as can deep colours like wine, burgundy and chocolate brown.

LIPSTICK TEXTURES AND FORMULAS

To find the perfect lipstick, it is important to understand the texture and establish the type of coverage you want to achieve.

Find the perfect texture

Gloss gives a 'wet look' and comes in a variety of high to low sheens and countless colour options. Wear it alone, with a lip pencil or over lipstick. It protects the lips by retaining essential moisture, but is not long lasting and needs regular touch ups.

Stains come in a liquid formulation and give lips a natural finish - almost like they've been stained with berries or red wine.

Cream lipsticks give an opaque coverage with very little shine. They contain silicones, which ensure easy application.

Matte lipsticks usually stay in place for longer as they offer a flat colour with the most coverage and maximum pigment content. However, this texture can be drying and can draw attention to fine lines. It's a great option for those of you who have a problem with colour 'bleeding' outside the lip line. To avoid dryness, dab on some lip balm before application.

Sheer lipsticks are ultra-light in texture and provide a tint of colour with a hint of shine. They stay on longer than gloss and are great for use in the summer, thanks to their added nourishing ingredients.

Long lasting formulas will stay put for the entire day as they contain special conditioning ingredients that cling to the lips. They can be wiped off with an oil-based make-up remover.

Shimmery lip colour with iridescent sheen reflects light to draw attention to the lips. These can give an illusion of a fuller pout.

LIP LINER

Lip liners typically come in pencil-form and are applied around the perimeter of the lips to add definition and prevent colour from bleeding. If applied incorrectly, it can look very unnatural, but correct application enables you to change the shape and size of the lips, as well as adding definition.

LIP LINER TIPS

- Liner gives a more polished finish to the lip area. Just remember to apply it prior to lipstick application.

- Avoid using a liner that is darker than your lipstick. If the lipstick fades you will be left with a dark outline, which can look very unattractive. Use a neutral liner or one that matches your lipstick and blend well to avoid an unpleasant outline when the colour fades.

- Before applying liner, smudge the sharpened pencil at the back of your hand to soften the pointy tip, this gives a natural looking outline.

- Starting at the centre of your upper lip, draw a line towards each outer corner. Following the edge of your natural lip line, using small feathery strokes.

- For extra holding power, you can fill in liner colour all over the lips before applying lipstick.

ACHIEVING FULLER LIPS

If you haven't been blessed with a full pout or have lost volume with age, here are some options for achieving volumous lips.

Semi-permanent make-up involves injecting hundreds of tiny colour pigment dots around the natural shape of the lip to create an almost tattoo-like lip line. This is an ideal option for older women who want to eliminate the problem of lipstick bleeding. It can create an illusion of a lift, by giving a youthful definition and fullness to the pout. It can also give uneven lips a balanced shape. Remember to consult a reputable therapist.

Collagen injections are used to plump up the lips. Results are short term and usually last for up to six months. Collagen can cause allergic reactions if it is not administered correctly. A consultation is essential before treatment.

Lip plumpers offer a simple way of achieving fuller lips. Heat-activating and stimulanting ingredients, such as cinnamon, ginger, cayenne pepper or even niacin work by warming up the skin tissue, causing capillaries to expand you are left with a subtle plumping feeling and a 'bee-stung' pout. Also found in modern lip plumps is maxi-lip technology, which is made from collagen and sits under the epidermis, trapping moisture and improving the fullness of the lip. Some plumpers can cause a slight tingly feeling, but this is common and nothing to worry about.

How to create fuller lips

Make-up artist Mehera Khola says, "Use light colours with lots of gloss to add fullness to the lips."

Steps to creating fuller lips

Ensure lips are soft and supple by using a lip balm - 15 minutes before colour application.
Cover the lip line with a foundation and powder it well. This provides an even surface for application and also helps to seal in colour.

1 Outline the lips just outside of the natural lip line. Ensure that the liner tip is touching the natural lip line - don't take it too far as it can look fake.

2 Ensure there are no gaps by filling in the remainder of the lips using light strokes of the pencil.

3 Use a brush to fill in the lips with a sheer lipstick or gloss - making sure to blend in the lip line.

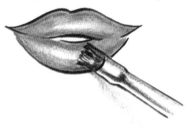

4 Dab a touch of highlighter to the centre of the bottom lip. This creates a wonderful 3D effect and an illusion of fullness.

DuWop LIP VENOM spicy gloss . gloss épicé 3.5 ml

How to create thinner lips

For those of you who want to achieve a thinner pout, try using darker colours, which can help to decrease your lip size. Plums and burgundies are your best bet. Avoid glosses or shimmers, which can inflate the lip size.

Follow these steps:

1 Cover the lip area with a foundation to provide a base for colour application.

2 Use a lip pencil to trace all the way around the inside of the lip line.

3 Fill in the lips. Your lipstick colour choice is important here. Select darker shades in a matte texture, which will absorb light and give the lips a smaller appearance.

How to reshape uneven lips

Apply foundation over the entire lip area and blot with powder. Using a sharpened pencil a shade or two darker than your natural lip tone, outline the lips to the desired shape. Start from the outer corner and finish at the middle.

LIP CARE TIPS

Have you ever wondered why our lips become dry and chapped? The main reason is that unlike other areas of the body, the lip dermis doesn't contain hair follicles or sweat glands, which means the lubricating effects of sebum are not present. As a result, lips are a lot more vulnerable to drying and chapping.

Lips require constant tender, loving care to keep them healthy and hydrated. These tips will keep them in top condition.

- For softer lips during cold winter months, use a petroleum-based product such as Vaseline or the models' favourite Elizabeth Arden's Eight-Hour Cream. These products work to seal in moisture and protect against external aggressors.

- If chapped and flaky lips are a problem, nibbling at them can make them worse. Use a soft toothbrush and gently brush across the lips in small strokes. This will remove flaky skin and leave you with a smoother pout.

- To prevent lips from becoming dehydrated, drink plenty of water and avoid lip licking. Constant licking only makes the condition worse as when the saliva evaporates, it draws moisture from the lips.

- Apply a generous coating of lip balm before bed. for an overnight moisture boost.

- Whenever you expose yourself to the sun use a lip protection balm, preferably one that contains a SPF of at least 15 to protect against dehydration and burning.

- Lips are naturally inclined to dryness during the winter months. Try applying a base coat of lip balm prior to applying lipstick.

GET THE LOOK

How to create matte lips by Ruby Hammer

Steer clear of this look if your lips are prone to dryness and cracking.

1 Prepare lips really well by exfoliating and then moisturizing them thoroughly.

2 After you have prepared the lips you can choose to apply your colour straight from the bullet, or for greater control and shape use a lip brush.

3 If your lipstick is more of a cream finish then, after application, pull apart some tissue and lay one thin ply over the mouth. Dust translucent powder over the ply before removing it - this will mattify the colour and add staying power.

How to create classic red lips by Nina Haider

Choose whether you want to go for a matte or glossy finish.

1 Moisturize the lips with a balm.

2 Use a neutral coloured pencil to outline and and then fill in the lips.

3 Apply a creamy-textured colour in a warm red tone. It is important to use a good quality lip brush for application accuracy. Blot with a tissue and then reapply. The first application will stain the lips for longer lasting staying power and the blotting will prevent colour from bleeding.

4 Finish with a sheer gloss for extreme glamour or leave them gloss-free for a classic Hollywood finish.

How to create glossy lips by Cory Wallia

Gloss can be used in several ways. MAC Lip Glass is my favourite.

1 Use a pencil to outline and fill in the lips.

2 Swipe on some gloss for a high-sheen pout.

3 For a softer finish, use gloss by itself.

How to create berry stained lips by Cory Wallia

1 Exfoliate the lips to create a smooth surface, then dab on some balm.

2 Use a lip lining pencil in a burgundy, red or magenta shade quite liberally all over the lips.

3 Leave it on for 5-10 minutes and then wipe it off, leaving the stain behind.

How to create nude lips by Nina Haider

Nude lips are understated, sexy and a perfect accompaniment for strong eye make-up.

1 Eliminate flaking by gently rubbing lips with a damp flannel, then prime them with a balm or foundation.

2 Line the lips with a pencil in a similar shade as your selected lipstick. Steer clear of darker or contrasting colour, which can take away the naturalness of the look.

3 Using a brush, paint on the lip colour and be sure to blend in the liner. You can even use your fingers for appliction - this enables the lip texture to show through for a more natural result.

4 To create glossy nude lips simply swipe on a clear gloss.

Be careful when selecting a shade. If you pick the wrong nude you could end up looking like a corpse.
Fair skin tones should opt for nude pinks or nude browns.
Medium tones look best with soft fleshy pinks and nude beiges.
Dusky complexions can carry nude beiges and fleshy pinks.

LIPPY TIPS

- Store your lipstick in the refrigerator - it will last longer.
- To avoid lip colour getting on your teeth after application, pop your index finger through the middle of your lips and pull it out. The excess will come off on your finger, not your teeth.
- Don't throw away old lip colours when they begin to fade down. Instead scrape out the remainder and place it into an empty lip palette - you can then mix and match to customize your own colour.

CHAPTER EIGHT
HANDS & FEET

HANDS & NAILS

When it comes to beauty, every tiny detail matters and giving your hands and nails some special attention will complete a well-groomed look.

HAND AND NAIL CARE TIPS

These tips will take you from ragged to refined in no time.

- A poor diet will affect nail growth - eat foods high in calcium for long-term healthiness.

- Wear cotton-lined rubber gloves when washing dishes or using cleaning detergents. Gloves help protect the hands and nails from drying out.

- Stop abusing your nails. Don't use them as tools to pick and poke at things.

- Treat your nails gently and moisturize them regularly. Replenish lost moisture by rubbing in some warm jojoba oil. Healthy cuticles not only improve the overall appearance of the nail, but also promote growth.

- If you have weak nails, try to keep them short, square-shaped and slightly oval on top. Only trim brittle nails after a bath or a 15-minute hand-soak.

- Rub some rich hand-cream into the hands and nails, cover with cotton gloves and leave overnight. You will wake up with hands that look and feel beautifully soft and smooth.

- Avoid acetone based polish removers, which can dry out the nails. Having said that, acetone removers work best when it comes to banishing really stubborn, dark polish. Just don't use them too often.

- If you've run out off remover resist the temptation of peeling or scraping off your polish. It can damage the protective cells of the nail surface.

- When having a salon manicure, ensure that the nail technician properly sterilizes all tools used.

A few tips especially for all you nail nibblers.

Nail biting is destructive to both the nail and the cuticle and can lead to infections that can actually deform the nail and cause uneven growth.

Keep a nail file handy at all times, when you notice a snag, use it, instead of your teeth.

Get a professional manicure. If you pay for one, chances are you'll be less likely to destroy it with your teeth.

You might have been looking for a magical way to stop biting your nails, but I'm afraid there's no such thing. You simply have to put your mind to it and stop!

CUTICLE CARE

Resist cuticle snipping. The main purpose of the cuticle is to protect the lunula (this is the moon-like semi circle at the base of your nail) against bacteria and fungi. Cutting them will only make them more ragged in the long term and may lead to infection.

Don't neglect them altogether, soak hands in soapy water for around five minutes and then push cuticles back with a manicure stick. Always use a cotton-tipped manicure stick as using an unpadded one can tear the cuticle. Finally massage some cuticle cream to the base of the nails on a daily basis to stimulate circulation and promote quicker nail growth. If you don't have a cuticle cream - olive oil, eye cream or even lip balm will help keep them hydrated.

NAIL SHAPE

Most manicurists will agree that the most flattering shape for the nail is a cross between square and oval. If filing your own nails just remember that the tip of your nail should match the curve of your nail base.

The best way is to clip the nails straight across, then round of the corners with a file. Don't file the nails in a zig-zag motion because this gives you less control and can cause splitting. File them in one direction, starting from the outside towards the middle.

Anjana's Top Tip!

Give your nails a break - Don't wear false nails for more that 3-4 weeks at a time. Keeping them permanently covered can lead to problems such as cracking and discolouration. Give your nails at least two days to breathe between applications.

IF THEY DON'T GROW - HERE ARE YOUR OPTIONS

Acrylic nails

Technicians claim that these are the strongest and most long lasting of all nail overlays. A false nail is fixed mid way up the natural nail. It is then buffed to remove any ridges and filed into shape. Next, the nails are coated with a mixture of a special powder and paste that is moulded into shape. They will then be buffed, smoothed and polished.

Why choose acrylics?

Acrylics are great for nail biters. The main reason being, you won't want to bite expensive and exquisitely designed nails! With acrylics you can choose your length and go as long or short as you like.

Gel nails

These are the most popular choice of nail extensions as the finish can look almost like your own. The false nail is glued to the middle of the natural nail. It is then buffed, smoothed, cut and shaped. Next, a thick polish-like gel is applied to the entire nail, which is allowed to set under an ultraviolet light where it hardens and leaves you with a set of strong nails.

Why choose gels?

Gels give you a more natural looking and light weight finish, which is an ideal fix for those with broken or weak nails. When applied and removed professionally, gels will do little damage to your natural nail.

Fibreglass nails

This is a great option for those of you with nails that break easily. Fibreglass strips are cut into the desired shape and glued to the nail plate. These will add strength and, in some cases, length to the nail. Fibreglass can also be used to salvage a torn nail.

Why choose fibreglass?

An ideal option if you have brittle nails or for those wanting to strengthen the nail tips. Fibreglass helps to protect the nail and allows them to grow without breaking.

Off-the-shelf nails

These can be applied in the comfort of your own home. They usually come with their own adhesive and can be cut and shaped into your desired choice. The only drawback is that these come in a standard size so may not be a perfect fit or look as natural as the other options.

Why choose Off-the-shelf nails?

They are quick and easy to apply and are reasonably priced.

How to get the perfect polish by Ketan Patel

1 Start with a perfect manicured nail. Clean all ten nails with a scrub to remove any oils and dust; this will allow your base coat to really stick to the natural nail.

2 Always use a base coat, not only will it help enamel to stick better, but it also prevents chipping and protects the nail from discolouring.

3 Using a three-stroke application for the base coat, start with a smooth stroke down the centre of the nail, then one stroke to the left and one stroke to the right. Make sure you run the end of the brush along the free edge of the natural nail.

4 Wait 60 seconds before applying your chosen colour. Once again use the same application method as your base coat for applying your enamel. Remember the first coat is for coverage, so make sure you apply it thinly. This will help with the drying process.

5 The second coat of colour is for adding depth and filling in any patches. Remember to run the brush along the free edge of the natural nail. Wait 60 seconds.

6 Now seal the enamel with a fast setting or high shine top coat. The use of a quality top coat is vital as this will seal the enamel and prolong the life of your manicure.

7 Now comes the detailing. Buy a thin artist's watercolour paint brush (available in any arts and crafts stores) and dip this into your polish remover. Use this to gently swipe and eliminate any accidents of colour you may have made on your skin. The brush will give you meticulous colour detailing and ensure your nails look truly professional. You can also use a thin wooden manicure stick with some cotton wool wrapped around the end to achieve a similar (but not as professional) result.

Must-have nail tools

Nail file
Use to remove rough edges and to file the nail into the desired shape.

Nail buffer
This is similar to a nail file but has a much smoother surface. Use it to polish and smooth the nail bed for a pearly gleam. Buff nails rapidly in one direction, using even motions.

Cuticle cream
Never work on a dry nail. Prepare the cuticle with a cream, which will work to soften and condition the area. Gently push the cuticle back using a padded manicure stick.

Hand cream
Keep hands looking and feeling beautifully soft and smooth with daily use of a hand cream. Use one containing SPF to inhibit signs of photo-ageing from UV exposure.

Nail polish remover
Use an acetone-free remover, which won't strip natural moisture away from the nails.

Base coat and top coat
Apply a clear base coat, preferably one that also fills in ridges. This will give you a smooth surface for polish application. A clear top coat will extend the life of nail colour and give a protective shine.

Anjana's Top Tip!
Rub some nourishing almond oil onto the cuticles and skin surrounding the nails before bed. It works like nail food to hydrate, strengthen and encourage growth.

FABULOUS FEET

Our poor feet get more hammering than any other part of the body. We stand on them all day and keep them trapped inside shoes, yet they are the most forgotten part of the body when it comes to pampering.

Foot guru Bastien Gonzalez shares his tips for healthy feet for life.

CORNS AND CALLUSES

Corns and calluses are most often found on the balls of the feet, the tops of toes, on the heels and even along the sides of the toenails. Calluses occur when pressure placed on the foot becomes out of balance causing extra friction on particular areas. The body responds to this intense strain by producing thick and hard patches of skin. If the cause of this pressure is not relieved, calluses can become painful. Banish calluses with a foot file, if you need something more vigorous try a microdermabrasion pedicure.

Corns appear when this strain becomes concentrated in a small area. Never cut corns yourself. Seek professional advice - a registered podiatrist or chiropodist will be able to remove them painlessly. Use padding or insoles to relieve short-term pressure.

HEALTHY NAILS

Keep toenails short by cutting or filing. Filing is important for smoothing away rough edges. To keep the nails in perfect condition, try not to overdo it with the polish as it can dry the nail bed and stop the growth from flourishing. If you can't resist dark varnish, try to give nails an occasional rest - coloured polishes have a strong pigment content that can stain the nail to a yellowish shade. For superb shine my secret is to buff the nails with a chamois leather cloth - it's far superior than a nail polish.

Treat your nails to a hydrating oil massage as often as possible, this will also keep the cuticles nourished. After bathing, brush the sides of the nails and cuticle to help slough away dead skin.

NOURISH THEM

The skin on the feet is much thicker than the rest of the body, so invest in a rich foot cream, don't rely on a body cream - it won't penetrate as effectively.

MASSAGE

Regular massage works wonders to stimulate circulation, relax the feet and relieve stressed soles after a hard day. It also improves muscular flexibility, joint mobility and skin elasticity. Use stroking movements in an upward direction.

If you suffer from heel pain, arch strain or foot cramps, try rolling a golf ball under the ball of your foot for two minutes. It's a great strain reliever for the soles.

FOOTWEAR

You can wear whatever shoes you choose to as long as you take care of your feet. High heels throw weight onto the balls of the feet, which can lead to calluses, corns and painful bunions. Try to vary your shoes from day to day - wear low heels one day and slightly higher the next. If you must wear heels on a daily basis, limit the size to a maximum of four centimeters.

High heel lovers should do some calf stretches every evening, they help to keep the feet supple and maintain a good range of movement. To stretch your calfs and heels, stand facing a wall with feet hip width apart and slightly bent at the knee. Take one step forwards, and using your arms to lean against the wall, keep your leg in front bent and the leg behind straight. Both feet should be flat on the ground. Lean in towards the wall, as you do, you should feel your muscles stretching in the calf and heel. Hold and slowly return to a standing position. Do this with each leg around five times. If you're a pointy shoe wearer be sure to stretch your toes at the end of the day to get the joints moving again. If you're going to continue wearing killer heels, it's worth adding a good chiropodist to your address book.

DIY HOME PEDICURE TIPS

If you don't have time for a regular in-salon pedicure, some home maintenance is essential.

1 Soak feet in slightly salted water to sterilise and soften the cuticles.
2 File away hard skin with a foot file.
3 Scrub the feet with an exfoliator to slough away tough skin. Rinse away residue.
4 Finish by slathering on a foot cream to soften dry soles. For an intensive foot treatment, pop on a pair of cotton socks after applying the cream and leave on overnight.

CHAPTER NINE
HAIR

HAIR

Hair experts put South Asian hair under the same bracket as Oriental hair, as both types have an almost perfect round shape with a straight or slightly wavy shaft. It is commonly dark brown or black in colour and is thicker in diameter and stronger than hair of any other ethnicity.

Hair expert Philip Kingsley says: "South Asian hair has a capacity to grow to a greater length than any other race - often over 40 inches." It is no wonder then, that as far back as we can remember, Indian women have been associated with long, lustrous locks. The beautiful heroines of the ancient Indian epics - Sita of the Ramayana, and Draupadi of the Mahabharata, the women depicted in the Kamasutra or in the paintings from the Moghul era - are all pictured with endless flowing locks.

Hairstylist Adhuna Bhabhani Akhtar says: "From a cultural point of view, long hair has always signified vitality and life. Even now, most modern women love to show off longer hair on occasions when they are wearing traditional outfits. The Indian male also seems to prefer their women with longer tresses. Although it is not true for all, but the majority for sure."

Did you know?

- Asian hair has the roundest circumference and is usually straighter, smoother and stronger. The flatter the hair strands (by cross section), the curlier it is. Caucasian hair is oval-shaped and Afro-Caribbean hair is flat.

- Our hair has a growth cycle of up to seven years, often resulting in waist length hair of 42 inches long.

- Indian women tend to over brush their hair. Over brushing can pull it out and cause breakage.

- Our hair, when young, is thicker and stronger than most. However, there appears to be a greater tendency for it to thin during pre and post-menopause years.

CARING FOR LONG HAIR

For those with long hair, devoting some time to care for it, is a must if you want it to look healthy and shiny.

Follow these tips by hairdresser Dar

• To maintain hair health, get it trimmed regularly (every 8-10 weeks is ideal) to help promote natural bounce and remove split ends.

• Use a good quality shampoo and conditioner. The Kerastase range is an absolute favourite of mine.

• If the texture of your hair is naturally dry and brittle, I highly recommend a deep conditioning treatment or some hair oil. Simply massage into the hair and wrap in a hot towel and leave for 20-30 minutes. This helps the conditioning ingredients to penetrate deeper.

Hair doctor, Philip Kingsley shares his wisdom

• It is important to minimize moisture loss in long hair - Indian hair can look quite stunning when it's in good condition. The use of moisturizing products and treatments is therefore essential, especially if the hair is long. Look out for the terms 'moisturizing', 'remoisturizing' and 'deep conditioning'.

• If your long hair is fine and limp, wash it with volumizing shampoo and use a good conditioner on the ends only.

• Use a remoisturizing pre-shampoo conditioner at least once a week, as longer hair is older hair so moisture and elasticity should be replenished. A protective and moisturizing serum should be applied to the ends of the hair (the oldest part).

COMMON HAIR PROBLEMS

Dry and brittle hair

Hair can be dry for a variety of reasons. In airconditioned enviroments the sebaceous glands can produce less of the hair's protective oils, leading to dryness. Curly hair can also be prone to dryness because the oil rests at the roots. Over processing the hair through chemical treatments such as perms and colouring, as well as over use of heated styling tools such as dryers and straighteners are also prime culprits.

Dry hair is vulnerable to losing moisture, therefore it needs extra care and plenty of nourishment. Be sure to condition after every wash. Spend time massaging the conditioner in with your fingers ensuring an even coverage. Combing conditioner through with a wide toothed comb will help the active ingredients penetrate deep into the cuticle.

Moisturizing shampoos and weekly use of an intensive conditioner can make an immediate difference.

The sun can be disastrous for dry hair. If you live in a hot climate, use a deep conditioner or give yourself regular oil massages to feed the locks with much needed moisture. If you are about to visit a hot holiday destination - start using conditioning packs two weeks before you go to prepare the hair for the onslaught of sun exposure.

Hairdryers, straightening irons and tongs should be avoided whenever possible. If using these tools is essential, be sure to apply a heat protection spray. When blow-drying, keep the hairdryer moving and the nozzle pointing down the hair shaft to keep the cuticles flat.

Air conditioning and central heating can create an extremely dry atmosphere, which will soak up essential moisture from the hair. Serums and styling aids can help provide a barrier against moisture loss.

Oily hair

Greasy hair can be caused by over-stimulation of the sebaceous glands. Here's what you can do to de-grease.

Wash your hair using a high quality frequent-wash shampoo. The frequency of washing depends entirely on your preference.

When shampooing, massage the hair gently using the palm of the hand. Avoid using the fingertips, as these will stimulate the scalp further.

Keep conditioners away from the roots - focus on the mid lengths and ends of the hair.

Specialist oily scalp treatment shampoos are great for occasional use.

Too much brushing of the hair can stimulate the already over active oil glands, so go easy.

Fine hair

Limp, wispy, flyaway hair can be a real nightmare for many women. Here are a few options on how to add body.

Look for labels containing the terms 'body-building', 'thickening' and 'volumizing'. Limpness originates at the roots of the hair so use sprays and mousses mainly on this area.

Don't over-use conditioner. Choose one that is formulated for limp hair. Heavy formulas can flatten it further. Avoid applying conditioner to the roots and concentrate on mid lengths and ends.

Hairstylist Asgar says: "Clever blow-drying can add body to fine hair. Apply a volumizing spray to damp roots. Flip your hair forward (so it is hanging in front of you). With a hairdryer, gently rough dry the hair using a brush or your fingers concentrating on the roots and following the direction in which the hair has fallen. Flip the hair up and continue to dry and style using a large round bristled brush. You will be surprised by the extra bounce."

Highlighting and introducing different tones to the hair can create the illusion of thickness. Your colourist will be able to advise what is best for you.

Frizzy hair

Both straight and curly hair can be affected by frizziness and taming it can be a real battle.

Frizzy hair is commonly dry. It can be naturally dry or become that way as a result of chemical treatments such as perming or colouring. Overuse of heated styling appliances can also contribute.

The wavier or curlier the hair, the frizzier it tends to be. If your hair has even the slightest wave or curl, it is susceptible to frizz. Why? because the protective oils do not reach the full length of the hair shaft which causes the protective outer cuticles to open up where the hair kinks.

When towel-drying, don't rub or create any sort of friction. The best method for drying frizzy hair is to firmly squeeze-dry it, from ends to roots.

Split ends can create frizzy fly-aways - have regular trims to prevent them. Split ends can travel up the hair strand, which provokes the frizz.

If you have curly hair, avoid brushing and use a wide-toothed comb instead.

Hair is also prone to frizziness in climates that change quickly. For example, you may be in a country where the air is dry in the morning but humid in the afternoon. This can be problematic.

Use styling products that discourage moisture absorption into the hair shaft. These include serums, which can dramatically improve the appearance and texture of fizz-prone hair. Ideally you should apply serum to damp hair before styling. Use a pea-sized amount on the mid-lengths to the ends. Be sure to use it sparingly, overuse can leave it greasy.

Split ends

The hair splits when the protective cuticle has been stripped away from the ends of the hair fibres. Split ends are more likely to develop on hair that is dry and brittle and is also common on locks that have been exposed to excessive heat styling damage or vigorous brushing.

Here's how to stop those horrid splits from spoiling your locks

· Resist over brushing since it promotes breakage. Never brush wet hair; instead detangle using a wide-toothed comb and start from the bottom up.

· Hairdryers, straightening irons, curling tongs, perming, and colouring can all affect the condition of the hair in a negative way. If blow-drying is a must, make sure you use a cool setting and keep the dryer a healthy distance away.

· Protect hair from extreme weather. Wear a hat on sunny days and keep your hair well moisturized during the dry winter months.

· Keep hair strong by applying a leave-in conditioner or pomade to the ends. Conditioners can help to mask the split end (by temporarily gluing them together).

· Have regular trims, particularly if your hair is long. Longer hair needs more care and is also more prone to splitting. This is largely due to what Philip Kingsley describes as the 'weathering effect' on hair that has been there for longer. Split ends will travel up the hair all the way to the scalp, so snip them off as soon as you spot them. Remember, the only way to heal a split end is to cut the hair above the split.

Dealing with dandruff

Dandruff is a very broad term used for scalp flaking. The skin all over the body sheds all the time as a form of natural cell replacement. This skin shedding also occurs on our scalp and leads to 'shoulder flaking'. You could have the common loose flakes, which most people can experience at some point in their lives or the more stubborn form that can cling to the hair shaft and at worst, lead to hair loss. "The first mistake when dealing with dandruff is to associate it with a 'dry scalp' or even dry skin. The fact is, it is mostly found in people with oily skin," says Philip Kingsley.

The most common form of dandruff is known as pityriasis capitis simplex. Most sufferers have this type and it generally flares up during times of stress. Most cases of dandruff are treated with an over-the-counter anti-dandruff shampoo. Look for active ingredients such as Zinc Pyrithione, Climbazole, Octopirox, and Ketoconazole. If your dandruff is inflammatory, itchy, or unusually severe, your doctor can prescribe a stronger solution.

Excessive hair loss

A number of factors including stress, diet, hereditary, hormonal imbalances and the use of certain medications can cause hair loss. However, once the root of the problem is established it is usually relatively easy to treat.

· Use of certain medications can cause temporary hair shedding. If you feel that your medicine is causing your hair to shed, seek advice from your doctor, who may be able to prescribe an alternative.

· Both an overactive and underactive thyroid gland can cause hair loss. This type of loss can be reversed with proper treatment.

· Many women may lose some hair approximately three months after giving birth. During pregnancy, high levels of certain hormones cause the body to keep hair that would normally fall out. When the hormones return to pre-pregnancy levels, this hair falls out and the normal cycle of growth begins again.

· A severe illness, surgery or significant levels of stress can cause hair loss. This condition usually corrects itself but may require treatment.

· People with abnormal eating habits, crash dieters and some vegetarians, may develop protein malnutrition. When this happens, hair loss is a common outcome, but can be solved by increasing your intake of protein. Vegetarians should substitute meat with other protein-rich foods, such as pulses, cereals, dairy products and nuts.

· The medical term given to male or female-pattern baldness is androgenic alopecia and this is the most common type of hair loss. The hair usually begins to thin at the front of the scalp and gradually moves to the back and top of the head. This type of hair loss is often hereditary and although there is no cure for it, prescription treatments are available. If adequate treatment is not available for your type of hair loss, you may consider trying different hairstyles, wigs, hairpieces, weaves or even hair transplants.

HAIR FAQ'S

Q. How can I boost my hair growth?

Hair grows from a follicle on the scalp and each follicle produces only one strand of hair. The average person has between 100,000 and 150,000 strands of hair on the head and the average hair grows at a rate of a quarter of an inch to half an inch each month. Yes, growing your locks can take some time and patience, but combine a healthy diet with hair care and you will soon see the results.

The following may boost growth:

Feed your Hair: Hair nutrition is vital for healthy growth. Nutritionists advise healthy hair seekers to eat a well-balanced diet that incorporates proteins along with foods high in vitamin A, B, C, E, and K.

Protein is the most important ingredient for promoting growth since hair is basically 98 per cent protein. Thus a diet that lacks protein may cause thinning or stunting of the growth cycle.

Your body requires two essential fatty acids, omega-3 and omega-6. These are not produced naturally by the human body but can be found in foods such as tofu, fish, raw nuts, seeds, and grains as well as oils such as sunflower, sesame and corn. A diet rich in fruits and vegetables plus plenty of water is also essential for beautiful long hair.

No matter how keen you are on growing your hair, a regular trim, every six to eight weeks, is essential. It does not have to be a dramatic cut, just snipping off split ends, which can cause the hair to break is enough.

Q. How often should I wash my hair?

The expert advice differs between daily to every other day. The common sense solution is to wash it when it feels and looks like it needs a wash, be that daily or twice weekly.

Philip Kingsley suggests the following:

It is impossible to over wash hair as long as the correct shampoo is used in the correct way; it will not strip the hair of necessary moisture.

Dry and brittle hair should be washed every three to four days so that it does not get robbed of its natural oils. You can leave it even longer if you don't have oily roots. But always use a moisturizing shampoo (ask your hairdresser to recommend the right one for your hair type). Use leave-in conditioners, or if you prefer a rinse out conditioner, also use a protective hairdressing spray.

Oily hair should be washed every other day to prevent it from looking too greasy. Use mild shampoos, as they won't strip away the hair's natural oils. If the scalp is oily and the ends are dry, then apply conditioner only to the dry areas.

When it comes to washing, the only difference between longer and shorter hair is the amount of shampoo and conditioner you use. Obviously shorter hair needs less product.

Q. Why does my hair not grow beyond a certain length?

Philip Kingsley explans the various reasons for this:
- It is trimmed too often.
- It breaks off at the ends as it grows from the roots.
- A metabolic disturbance affects the hair growth, and may cause it to fall out prematurely. This could be due to low iron levels, hormonal changes, nutritional problems, or thyroid irregularities.

Asgar advises: "A regular head massage will stimulate the scalp, get the circulation going and promote hair growth."

Dilshad Pastakia says. "A healthy lifestyle and a good diet comprising of essential fruits, vegetables and proteins will help. A regular trim is important - take off only a quarter of an inch on a regular basis and watch it grow."

HAIR EXTENSIONS

If you do not have the patience to grow your hair but want to have long locks in a hurry - your best bet is to fake it. Hair extensions are becoming increasingly popular and can give you length, volume or a hint of colour in as little as an hour.

Q. What hair is used in extensions?

There are two main hair types; synthetic and human.

Human hair is exactly what it states (it comes from a living person's head). The look and feel of this hair-type is the same as your own natural hair. It is available in a variety of textures and colours and is relatively easy to find an ideal match.

Synthetic hair is an artificial replica of human hair and is manufactured from man-made materials. It can sometimes look too shiny or give you a 'doll hair' like appearance.

So, which is better? This depends on personal preference. You can decide which is best for you, after taking into account factors such as cost, weight, application system, and duration of wear.

Q. How long does it take to apply the extensions?

"This all depends on the method of application and the desired effect," says Hair Extensions expert Patricia Akaba.

Some methods can take as little as 30 minutes and others can take up to six hours. The two most common methods are micro-bonding and weaving.

Micro-bonding is a method in which a small quantity of hair is attached with the same amount of extension hair and fused together away from the scalp using formulated glue and a heated applicator. This method is great for creating volume and length but the added weight can cause the hair to snap, so extra care should be taken when washing.

Weaving can work to add length and volume. Two or four rows of woven tracks can achieve the same look as a full head of micro-bonded extensions - in less than half the time. It is also better for the hair as no heat or glue is used. The look is achieved by cornrowing sections of hair and sewing on the extensions by a simple weaving procedure.

COLOUR

For years we have experimented with various natural techniques to create a change in hair colour. The most popular being henna, which when applied to the hair, gives often unnatural shades of red. Lemon juice, which works as a natural bleach when exposed to the sun, has also been used for similar purposes.

Fortunately now, a visit to the salon can give us a professional-looking finish. A change of colour or adding some highlights or lowlights is one of the quickest and most dramatic ways to transform our look. When hair is coloured, it is usually to shades of red or brown as these work well with dark hair. Some, however, choose to stand out from the crowd and be experimental with shades of copper and blonde.

Looking after coloured hair

Can hair colouring cause damage? It is a commonly asked question by colour virgins and the answer is yes and no. Any hair that has undergone dyeing is vulnerable to damage. The degree of damage, however, depends on the amount and frequency of colour change. For example, going from dark to extremely light can cause damage due to the strength of the bleaching agent. It is important to consider the condition of your hair before colouring. If your hair is damaged prior to colouring, it is likely be even more damaged after the process as repeated chemical altering can eventually affect the natural lustre and elasticity of the locks.

However, if you colour in moderation and follow the necessary precautions, the risk of damage is much less. Some of the modern chemical formulations are almost as gentle as their natural vegetable counterparts.

Colour care tips

• Ensure you upkeep the condition of coloured locks by using shampoos and conditioners specially formulated for colour-treated hair.
• UV light fades colour, so if your hair is regularly exposed to the sun, ensure you wash it with a shampoo containing relevant protectants.
• Use an intensive conditioner on a regular basis. It will help restore hair texture and reintroduce the vitamins that may have been lost by the colouring process.

TYPES OF COLOUR

Temporary colour: These are hair mousses or the small colour sachets you can buy from the chemist. They are great for adding a hint of colour, which lasts for up to three washes.

Natural colour: The best example of natural colour is henna. It leaves behind a reddish-copper hue and cannot be washed out. You will need to let it grow out.

Vegetable colours: True vegetable dyes are derived from natural ingredients such as herbs, plants, flowers and vegetable minerals. They are made into infusions and pastes. The colour sits on the hair's surface and can add incredible gloss and shine. This colouring method is only recommended for use on virgin hair.

Semi-permanent colours: These dyes are bleach-free so they can't lighten the hair colour. They can be used to change the tone of the hair by adding red, burgundy, gold, or copper hues. The colour will usually last between five to ten weeks and will fade each time the hair is washed. They are ideal for creating short-term bold fashion colours.

Permanent tints: These can be used to add an infinite variety of shades and can give complete coverage to grey hair. Working with peroxide, which lifts the hair colour, they enter the cortex of the cuticle, changing its shade. Roots will usually need re-touching every four to five weeks.

Highlights and lowlights: The difference between the two is quite simple. Highlights lighten and brighten the hair using tones of honey and caramel, whilst lowlights darken and deepen it using tones of red and plum. Almost any hairstyle and length can be highlighted or lowlighted and both are great options for updating your look without making a drastic change. Both are applied by methods of streaking, weaving, and foiling. They offer an interesting alternative to a single block of colour and are great for adding depth and texture to any hairstyle.
Remember that it is important to conduct a patch test, to check for any negative skin reactions, before using any form of hair colour.

How to get hair colour right

Adhuna Bhabhani Akhtar says: "The key here is to work with the natural skin tone and eye colour. Our hair is dark and seems to work best when it is not lightened too much. Going against the natural hair colour can be carried off by very few. Changing the tone of the hair can brighten up an already beautiful base shade. Reds, burgundies, and even various shades of brown can work extremely well."

Asgar advises: "The aim of colouring dark hair is to give it some lift and interest without going to extremes and making it too blonde. No one wants hair with too much contrast. The further you take the colour away from your base or normal colour, the more re-growth it will create, which will need regular root re-touching. The aim is to gently lift the hair colour but not create any garish gold or brassy effects."

Going blonde

It is commonly asked for, but what do the experts really think?
Adhuna Bhabhani Akhtar says: "It doesn't work with brown complexions and is totally going against Mother Nature. Our natural bases range from light brown to black, but most common is dark brown - so in order to get it completely right, one should not shift the natural base too far. Also, going this light will eventually start to take its toll on the condition of the hair."

Asgar says: "Colouring the hair, all over in one shade of blonde does not compliment women with brown skin, whose hair colour is naturally dark. However highlighting the hair with tones of honey and chestnuts can work and look very attractive."

HAIR COLOUR DO'S AND DON'TS

DO have a consultation. If you are a hair colour virgin, it is important to consult a professional colourist before going ahead.

DO choose your colour wisely to compliment the shape and style of your haircut.

DO use a shampoo and conditioner for chemically treated hair to maintain its optimum condition.

DO touch up your colour as recommended by your colourist to ensure it stays looking fresh all year round.

DON'T allow your roots to grow above one to two inches without touching them up - this looks ugly!

DON'T apply colour on top of colour.

DON'T copy someone else's hair colour. We all have different skin colouring, make-up styles, hair texture, and hairstyle. What works on one person may not look right on you.

OIL - AN ESSENTIAL HAIR CARE REMEDY

Oiling the hair has been a widely practised beauty ritual for thousands of years. Regular application of oil is said to prevent greying by maintaining the natural colour of the hair as well as enriching it. Oil massage on the scalp is extremely cooling and stimulating, which helps to promote healthy hair growth.

Coconut Oil is the most commonly used oil and is applied regularly to the scalp and hair by both men and women. It helps to keep the scalp moisturized, aids luxurious hair growth and strengthens thinning locks.

It is customary to allow the hair to soak up the oil overnight to reap the full benefits, but in today's fast paced lifestyle you can place a hot towel over the oiled hair, leave for three to four hours and wash. You will immediately notice the difference.

What the experts say

Adhuna Bhabhani Akhtar: "The application of oils to treat the hair and scalp has been used for centuries and in my opinion produces the same if not better results than their modern day convenient product substitutes."

Dar: "The most important thing we fail to do in the West is nourish the scalp. I believe this is an absolute must. We moisturize our face and body on a daily basis, so why not give our scalp the same treatment? In India and Pakistan we massage organic mustard and almond oil into the scalp and leave it on overnight (or at least for a couple of hours!). This provides the scalp with the necessary nourishment and moisture needed to make the hair healthier."

HAIR IN THE SUN

Like our skin, the hair also needs protection from the sun. The sun's powerful rays can burn, frizz and frazzle the hair. It can weaken its protein structure, which causes it to lack moisture and elasticity.

Follow these tips for protecting your hair from the sun

- While swimming or relaxing on the beach make sure hair is protected. There are plenty of effective sun protection sprays, leave-in conditioners and styling products that do a great job. If you are going for a swim, the combination of chlorine and UV rays can cause double the damage, so use a water resistant protective product.

- Wear suitable headgear - to gain optimum protection from the sun.

- Dark and chemically processed hair has a tendency to dry out faster. It is essential to retain its moisture levels by treating it to an intensive conditioner at least once a week. The ends of long hair are also prone to drying so keep them conditioned.

- If your hair is exposed to the sun on a daily basis use a shampoo and conditioner with UV protectants, as well as an intensive treatment at least twice a week to keep it nourished. Traditional warm oil application can also have the same benefits.

CHAPTER TEN
UNWANTED HAIR

UNWANTED HAIR

Society has always expected women to be smooth and fuzz free. Body and facial hair is considered unattractive and something which should be removed. For this reason, we are constantly using hair removal methods. From shaving to waxing to electrolysis, it is important to understand which technique is suited to particular areas of the body.

Excessive hair is quite common with South Asian women. Visible growth, particularly on the face, can shatter your confidence. But try not to despair, excess hair is no rare affliction. Did you know that a quarter of all women have visible hair on the face? And with newer hair-removal techniques developing as you read this, it needn't be a solution-less problem.

Before making an informed choice about the method of hair removal to opt for, it is important to understand the different types of hair on our face and body.

The facts

· All hair begin as vellus hair, which are tiny and almost colourless - you may be able to see these on the tip of your nose. The entire body and face is covered with thousands of these hairs, but they may not be visible as they are so small. The
root of a vellus hair is situated very close to the surface of the skin and the vast majority of them will stay like this throughout our life.

· A small number of these hairs are stimulated at birth and then later at puberty to become terminal hairs (visible hairs).

· Visible hairs can be split into two categories. The size of both these types of hairs can range from very thin to extremely coarse.

· Pre-puberty terminal hairs
These are found all over the face and body such as the eyebrows, scalp and arm area. The hair can vary in thickness and is usually the same colour as your natural scalp hair.

· Post-puberty terminal hairs
These mainly develop during puberty but may also continue to appear slowly well into your 20's and 30's. Most common areas include the underarms, lower arms and the pubic area.

Hair-removal expert Pamie Dhanoa says: "Various hair growth patterns can occur naturally without any medical condition present. This is important to understand as many articles on excess hair give the impression that anything but the lightest hair growth is the result of hormonal imbalance or some terrible illness. There is a big overlap of normal hair growth over abnormal growth, which is why hormonal problems are not usually diagnosed by hair growth alone. Abnormal hair growth is often accompanied by other health problems."

Did you know?

In the subcontinent, young mothers are taught to massage their baby daughters' skin with chickpea flour mixed with fresh cream to hamper later growth of body hair.

REASONS FOR HAIR GROWTH

If you have unwanted hair, it could be down to many factors.

It's genetic - your hair growth is likely to be similar to that of your parents or grandparents.

Facial hair can increase at the time of menopause when oestrogen levels begin to fall.

Abnormal hair growth is almost always a secondary symptom of a hormonal imbalance. Prolonged stress, dietary problems (obesity or too much processed food), and androgenic disorders are usually the culprits.

Unfortunately, it can be difficult to diagnose the root cause of abnormal growth. Once a follicle has been triggered to grow a hair, it will continue to produce them, even if the hormonal imbalance has disappeared. This is why male-to-female transsexuals do not lose their beards, even when taking boosters of female hormones.

Why are South Asian women hairier?

The main reason is that why we are particularly prone to unwanted hair is due to our genetic make-up. The racial mix of people migrating into Asia from centuries ago has in most cases, led to a type of growth pattern that includes more terminal hairs than western races. One theory is that our ancestors may have developed hair follicles, on an evolutionary-basis, as hair can provide protection from sun exposure.

IS YOUR GROWTH NORMAL?

Body hair

It is normal for women to have coarse growth around the nipples and on the chest. The pubic line continues up to the belly button so hair growth in this area is also natural. A few scattered coarse hairs can also prop up naturally on the upper back and shoulders. It is also common to find hair on the lower back (known as the triangle patch). Growth in this area is often hereditary. If however you have a more pronounced pattern of growth on your upper back and shoulders, which extends down to the middle of the back, you should seek medical advice.

Facial hair

Of all types of excess hair, facial hair seems to cause the most distress for obvious social reasons. It is very common to develop coarse hairs on the upper lip, chin, sideburns, neck, and chin area. If you experience heavy growth in these areas, it is usually a sign of hormone imbalance or an increased sensitivity to normal hormone levels. If you find your growth to be slowly increasing, visit your doctor who may prescribe you with medication to prevent this. Don't wait until the hair is fully developed as it is more difficult to remove than prevent.

Pamie Dhanoa says: "Rest assured you are not any less of a woman for developing beard hair. Every woman has the ability to grow hair in this pattern if she has a hormonal problem, so don't assume it is 'freakish'. The only reason it is not well known is because women tend to keep this type of problem a secret."

FIGHT THE FUZZ

The hair removal market offers a huge amount of choice for removing unwanted fuzz and the razor is no longer our only option.

Smooth operating methods

Threading involves using a cotton thread manipulated within the fingers of both hands to pull out unwanted hairs. It's best for shaping the brows and treating small areas such as the upper lip, chin and sides of the face. The first time can be painful, but once you get used to it you'll become immune. Expect to stay hair-free for almost three weeks.

Wet shaving is the easiest and cheapest method of hair removal and is best for the underarms and legs. Use a specially-formulated moisturizing shaving preparation such as foam, oil or gel beneath the razor blades. Shaving in the same direction as the hair growth is the most comfortable, however shaving against the hair growth certainly gives a much closer shave. Look for razors with safety guard wires over the blades to minimize the risk of cuts, nicks and irritation.

Epilators have an electric rubber roller or coiled spring that catches the hair and pulls it out. They can be used without water and are ideal for use on the legs, as even hair as short as 0.5mm can be banished. Avoid using on sensitive skin areas such as the face. Hair removal is quick and easy and stubble regrowth takes around two to three days.

Ingrown hairs

Ingrown hairs occur when the hair follicles become blocked by dead skin. The problem starts when hair is removed. When re-growth begins the new hair is blocked and begins to curl up inside the follicle. The hair doubles over itself making it impossible for it to break through to the surface. The only way to avoid the problem is to keep the area clean and exfoliated by using a scrub, loofah or body brush. Rubbing the area well using a towel after a bath or shower can also help.

Pamie Dhanoa adds. "Wait at least 15 minutes before applying moisturizer after a bathing, otherwise the follicles will become blocked. Follicles get gunked up more easily when the skin is still damp."

Chemical depilatories come in cream or gels formulas, then contain chemicals that dissolve the protein structure of the hair causing it to separate from the skin. It's a quick and pain-free method where the hair is removed from the skin's surface rather than the follicle, which means hair regrowth is quite quick - usually within a week to ten days.

Waxing is probably the most effective method of temporary hair removal. A wax combination is spread thinly over the skin. A cloth strip is pressed on the top and then pulled off with a sharp movement, removing the wax along with the hair. It can be used on most parts of the body (apart from the nipples, inside the ears and nose). It will keep you stubble-free for up to four weeks. Hair will also become finer with repeated use.

Sugaring is a technique that originated in Egypt. A paste made primarily of sugar is warmed and applied to the surface of the skin. The sugaring paste is then removed taking the hair with it. The method is similar to waxing but some find it less painful. Skin stays hair-free for approximatley four to six weeks.

Electrolysis is a professional, salon-based treatment. The process involves channelling a small electric current to destroy the hair root. Each hair has to be treated individually, so it is quite time consuming, a little painful and costly. It's best suited for small areas such as the upper lip, chin, and nipples. A few sessions are required before the hair disappears permanently.

Laser treatments involves a combination of different light wavelengths being emitted through a gentle beam of light that passes through the skin to destroy the hair follicle. Unlike electrolysis, it can treat multiple hair follicles simultaneously. You will need to find one that is suitable for darker skin and three to six sessions are required to ensure every last hair is destroyed.

Sound hair removal such as Epil-Pro, weakens hair growth by sending thousands of sound waves into the hair shaft. Unlike electrolysis it can be used on any part of the body and unlike laser, it works on all skin types and hair colour. It is non-invasive and virtually pain free. A course of four to six treatments is required until the re-growth ceases almost completely.

CHAPTER ELEVEN
BRIDAL BEAUTY

BRIDAL BEAUTY

Is there any more important day to look beautiful than that of your wedding? The wedding day for any bride is one of the most significant days in her life and this has been the case for hundreds of centuries. The build up to the day involves the practice of many beauty rituals that have been passed down through countless generations. It is the day where the bride's female relatives (including mother, sisters, aunts, and cousins) spend hours dressing, decorating and admiring her.

Emperor Shah Jahan's beloved wife Mumtaz Mahal's beauty ritual is probably the most well known. In her book, Beloved Empress Mumtaz Mahal, author Nina Epton describes the beauty rituals of the queen who inspired the Taj Mahal.

"A little before midnight Arjumand (later called Mumtaz Mahal) was given a ritual bath by her mother and various aunts. They escorted her to her bathroom wrapped in white cotton. Her long black hair was loosened, washed and her face bathed with the same herb infused water.

One of her aunts picked up an earthenware jar containing seven little balls of a creamy substance coloured blue, pink, red, green, yellow, white and orange (seven for luck). These were kneaded into a homogeneous mask and spread on Arjumand's face, neck and breasts, then washed off with perfumed soap.

The following morning was taken up with the bridal make-up, which took the palace experts nearly three hours to apply. Gold leaf was applied to her hairline; a golden dragonfly was impressed upon her forehead on a wax background. Her eyes were heavily underlined with kohl and prolonged by upward slanting strokes of the brush."

Ancient mythology, stories and paintings are full of references to these beautifying rituals and practices and have inspired us to follow and preserve the same customs and procedures till this very day.

Solah shringar… the modern version

The solah shringar (or sixteen adornments) is a traditional Indian beautification process that women still follow today. Some brides may even modernize the ritual to suit changing fashions and trends. The bride's solah shringar starts from the top with her hair and ends at the toes.

The sixteen adornments:

Bindi

The practice of wearing a bindi goes back centuries. The small red dot between the eyebrows and forehead traditionally symbolizes a woman's marital status. Today, the bindi has undergone a revamp and comes in a variety of shapes, colours and designs. Modern brides can choose bindis to match the exact colour of their dress and can even pick from an endless selection of intricate and elaborate designs adorned with diamonds, crystals, pearls, gold, or silver. These days the bindi is an elaboration of the bridal outfit and brides even have the option of personalized versions. It is also traditional for brides to have an extended bindi stretching across the forehead although this is mainly a Hindu practice.

Flowers in the hair - The bride's hair is oiled and adorned with tiny fragrant flowers such as jasmine. Modern brides have adapted the look by wearing a single decorative flower to add a pretty touch to summer weddings.

Kohl

Traditionally women would use home-made kohl to highlight and define the bride's eyes. Today it is easy to buy ready-made kohl. Thanks to advancements in cosmetics, we now have the option of kohl pencils in a variety of colours.

The upper and lower garment

In the ancient Vedic era, the upper garment was traditionally a narrow, long piece of cloth which was tied over the breasts and knotted at the back, much like a strapless bra. Today, brides wear different types of blouses to compliment their lehenga or sari. Hundreds of years ago, the lower garment was a cloth held up to the waist with a string used as a belt. Now, we have beautifully embroidered saris or lehengas in different styles and cuts to choose from.

Henna

Henna is a wedding must. The bride-to-be will have a "mehndiwali", or henna artist, attend the mehndi night (usually the night before the wedding) to apply designs onto her palms and feet. We still follow this ritual today. The henna night is attended by female friends and relatives who also have their hands painted. Henna is kept on overnight to achieve a richer colour the next morning. The resulting deep red colour is considered to be auspicious because it has several emotional, sexual and fertility-related qualities. Today, modern brides can further decorate and personalize their henna designs with the use of coloured glitter and bindis.

Fragrance

Traditionally brides would be perfumed with scents of rose, jasmine, sandalwood, and lemon. We can now spend hours at department stores selecting the perfect scent.

Sandalwood paste

The "pithi" ceremony is a ritual that brides still undergo to this day. Female family members will apply a paste of oil, turmeric and gram flour to a the face, arms and feet. The oil makes the skin supple, turmeric works as an antiseptic and the gram flour adds radiance.

Earrings, necklace, bangles, rings, armlets, waistbands, anklets, and toe rings

This jewellery is used by the bride to highlight and draw attention to her best features.

The significance of sindoor

Sindoor is vermilion (powdered red lead), which is applied for the first time to a woman during the marriage ceremony, when the bridegroom adorns her with it. Traditionally, it is applied in the parting of the hair and worn by women thereafter as a visible expression of their desire for their husbands' longevity. Hindu tradition believes that the goddess Parvati protects all those men whose wives apply vermilion on the hair parting.

HOW TO CHOOSE YOUR MAKE-UP ARTIST

Many brides prefer to have their hair and make-up on their wedding day taken care of by the professionals. It is the one day in your life where you can feel like a queen and why not be waited on by those who have the right expertise and tools to make you feel your radiant best? Brides-to-be often ask me how to find the right make-up artist and hair stylist. The majority of them say that they don't know where to start. Because these professionals can be costly it's important to know what to look for before you book. Here are some guidlines.

• Begin your search at least six months to a year in advance. Hair and make-up artists are in demand, especially during the bridal season when wedding dates can overlap. Secure your date well in advance to avoid disappointment.

• If you are unsure about how to go about looking for a make-up artist, the best thing to do is ask around. Speak to recently-married women, friends and family members, who will give you an honest recommendation. Flick through magazines and you may come across the work of artists you like. However, when doing this you must bear in mind that magazines often retouch images. So what you see may be an unfair representation of the make-up artist's work.

• Interview your artist - after all they are being hired to do a job. Ask to see a portfolio to get an idea of the looks he or she has created. They usually contain before and after shots of previous brides and will give you a good idea of their style of work. If the artist interviews you, this is a good sign. To do a good job, they need to know your daily make-up habits, the colour of your dress, the length of your ceremony and wedding day lighting. You should also provide them with pictures of specific looks you have in mind. All this will determine the type of make-up that is used on you. If your make-up artist is also doing your hair, or if you have a separate hair stylist, they should ask you specific questions about the neckline of your dress and may ask to see any accessories you may be using.

• Don't be afraid to ask what brand of make-up they use. You may have a particular favourite that works for your skin, especially when it comes to foundation. If you're worried about them not having the right colour match, don't be afraid to take your usual brand along with you to the consultation.

• Choose a bridal make-up artist who includes a pre-wedding consultation. The consultation or trial usually takes place months or weeks before the wedding day. The trial is important for both, you and the artist - it is almost like a make-up dress rehearsal. It is a time to be sure you get the look you want and will give you the opportunity to ask questions and make adjustments to the look as you go along. You can also see the final make-up look or hairstyle you will have on your wedding day. It eliminates the possibility of any horrible surprises, giving you one less thing to worry about.

• While it is important for your artist to respect your opinion and the way you would like to look, you should take their advice into consideration - remember that they are experts and they do it on a daily basis. Having said that, by no means should you feel intimidated or pushed into a look you are not happy with. The final look should be a collaboration between you, your make-up artist and hairstylist.

• Your makeup artist and hair stylist should be mobile and be willing to travel to wherever it is you are getting ready on the wedding day. The last thing you want to do is travel from one place to the other.

• Try to resist the temptation of booking a make-up artist who lacks experience, creativity and the patience necessary to create your desired look. Weddings can be costly but this is the last area you want to cut costs on. Ultimately, if you don't feel beautiful and confident, it will show - not only on the day, but for a lifetime in your photographs and wedding video.

• Wedding days can become chaotic and no matter how meticulously you plan, there is usually a slight hiccup. Choose an artist who has a calm and relaxed demeanour. After all, getting ready is part of the fun of the day.

SIX MONTH BRIDAL BEAUTY COUNTDOWN

In the midst of all that hectic activity - choosing wedding invitations, dresses, jewellery, florists and a honeymoon destination - you can easily forget your pre-wedding beauty regime of looking and feeling great. Unfortunately, a gorgeous glow won't just miraculously arrive in time for the big day and some prepping and planning is essential. Follow this time-line to make sure you are looking your wedding day best.

FIVE TO SIX MONTHS TO GO

Start prepping your skin. A good cleansing, toning and moisturising regime is important, as is a twice weekly exfoliation and face mask. If you are prone to breakouts, book an appointment with a dermatologist.

Start thinking about your diet. Increase your intake of fresh fruits, vegetables, lean proteins and high fibre foods. Cut back on junk food and caffeine. It will not only help your skin, but your digestion too.

Get in shape. If you're hoping to shed some pounds, set a weigh-loss target and meet it before your dress fittings. If you don't already, start exercising. Find a fitness regime that you are able to stick to until your wedding day. You may want to book a few sessions with a personal trainer who can help you jump-start your routine.

The posture enhancing, strength building and stress relieving abilities of yoga makes it a perfect option. As well as helping to shed pounds, cardiovascular workouts such as kickboxing or aerobics may also help to release built-up tension.

Start having trials with potential hair stylists and make-up artists. If you're unsure of how you would like your wedding day make-up, look at magazines for inspiration and tear out any looks you are keen on. Take a friend or family member with you for a second opinion and for taking photographs of you, which you can look back on at home.

Book your professionals and start planning your look. If you want to grow your hair, try a new style or change hair colour - talk to your hairdresser.

FOUR MONTHS TO GO

Start a regime of monthly facials. Skin cells renew themselves every 28 days, so this is a great treat for your complexion. You may get a few spots after the treatment, but there's no need to worry, this is the skin's way of getting rid of impurities.

THREE TO TWO MONTHS TO GO

Don't neglect your feet, especially if you're having a summer wedding or jetting off to a tropical honeymoon destination. After bathing, smooth feet with a scrub or foot file every few days, this will prevent the build up of rough skin. Massage them daily with a rich cream.

Get bikini ready. If cellulite is a problem, start regular skin brushing on problem areas such as the thighs and bottom to help rev up the circulation and lymph system. Now's the time to start using an anti-cellulite cream to ensure the product works to its potential.

Exfoliate your body at least once a week and don't forget your elbows, knees and feet. Silky soft skin is a wedding day must.

ONE MONTH TO GO

If water retention is a problem, daily lymphatic drainage massage can help. Beauty guru Bharti Vyas says: "Use the balls of your fingers in small circular movements to massage the entire body, then pinch the skin using all four fingers and thumb - this combination will help to stimulate the lymph systems, increase circulation and eliminate waste."

A sparkling white smile can make all the difference. Schedule a teeth cleaning appointment, start using an over-the-counter home whitening kit or you may even want to consider professional bleaching by a dentist.

If you don't already, get your eyebrows professionally shaped. It can make a big difference to your face.

ONE TO TWO WEEKS TO GO

Get your final haircut, trim and colour.

Remove any unwanted hair and don't forget the 'hair down there' - a groomed bikini area is a honeymoon essential.

Drink plenty of water to help flush out toxins and keep the skin looking clear and radiant.

Have your final facial. As with any detoxification process, spots can emerge, so avoid having one too near to your wedding day.

Treat yourself to a massage to help calm your body and mind.

If water retention is still a problem, book a body wrap, which involves the body being wrapped with bandages that have been pre-soaked in a detoxifying solution. Wraps can help to visibly slenderize the body and leave it feeling taut and toned. Confirm big-day beauty appointments.

THE DAY BEFORE

Don't neglect the finer details - have a professional manicure and pedicure.

Drink plenty of water.

Pack an emergency beauty kit such as oil blotting sheets, pressed powder, a nail file, mini hairspray, hair pins and lipstick. You'll need them for touch ups when your hair and beauty team leave. Don't forget a pack of tissues - there's bound to be tears.

Have a healthy meal and try to avoid alcohol and salt as these can contribute to under-eye puffiness.

Exfoliate your skin top-to-toe to ensure a wedding day glow.

Give your hair a moisture boost by using a deep conditioning mask or massage in a hair oil.

Take a long relaxing bath with a few drops of lavender oil to help induce a good night's sleep.

Get a good night's rest.

ON THE DAY

Have a hearty breakfast - you will need the energy throughout the day.

If you had difficulty sleeping, pop on an eye mask or white tea bags to reduce puffiness.

Give yourself plenty of time to glam up.

DIY BRIDAL MAKE-UP TIPS

If you fancy being your own make-up artist, here are a few handy pointers.

Shop around

Visit the make-up counters in department stores and take advantage of their free consultations. They can help you try a new look or give you some inspiration.

Day or night

Choose make-up that reflects the formality and the time of day of the event. Light, natural colours work at a casual daytime events, while bolder colours fit right in at night.

Start as you mean to go on

If you are doing your own make-up remember that foundation is the most important element of all. A medium coverage base is a good choice as it cover flaws and looks natural too. Remember to blend, blend, blend to avoid unsigthly streaks.

Be yourself

Your wedding day make-up should mirror who you are and how you look. Keep make-up similar to what you usually wear, but with a little more impact, definition and staying power.

Hide tiredness

If your eyes are red and tired from lack of sleep, eye drops can work to revive them. You can also use a white pencil on the lower rims of the eyelid.

Use a waterproof mascara

Wedding days are full of emotional tears. The last thing you want is smears on your cheeks.

Long wearing lips

Prep your pout to ensure maximum holding power. Outline the lips with a pencil and then scribble in the entire lip - this will serve as an anchor for the lipstick. Use a lip brush to apply a thin layer of colour - starting from the centre of the mouth, blending outward. Blot with a tissue, then apply another layer of colour.

COLOUR CHOICES

Traditionally, the bride's wedding outfit would be determined by where she came from. South Asian brides would opt for dark vibrant colours such as burgundy, red, green, and gold. Although these are still popular today, a wider variety of other colours have become more prominent in modern bridal outfits. Pastel shades of pink, blue and lilac - and even white or ivory - are now fashionable and acceptable.

The different ceremonies and functions associated with weddings can be spread over several days, which means you could be wearing a different outfit and embodying a different look for each occasion. Obviously forking out for a make-up artist for each ceremony can prove to be costly, so if you are planning to do your own make-up, I have tried to make it a little less harder for you by stealing the secrets of those-in-know.

Cory Wallia: "Since most Gujarati and Punjabi brides wear red and gold or magenta and gold there are some typical eyeshadow colours that are commonly used. Bronze, gold and copper are perennial favourites with brides. These shades set off the yellow pigment present in our skin really well, and also work beautifully with the jewellery and embellishments on the dress. There are a whole lot of metallic liquid eyeliners available that beautifully enhance the eyes. Try Barry M Dazzle Dusts and MAC Pigments - you are bound to find a colour to match your outfit."

Nabila: "When it comes to bridal make-up it is important not to lose your identity. Many brides make the mistake of wanting to look completely different. Of course it is one of the biggest days of your life where you will be centre of attention, wearing extravagant clothing, over-the-top jewellery and surrounded by lights, cameras and spectators. You want to look a little more grand than you usually would. However, the key is to keep the make-up and hair as simple as possible. You can wear lots of make-up but the look should appear like you hardly have any on. If you get your base right, the rest of the make-up only serves to enhance your features and your chosen outfit. My simple rule for a wedding-day base, is not to overdo foundation application, the aim is to achieve a fresh looking complexion".

"Other simple guidlines to remember are that if you have heavy eyes, the lips should be kept fairly subtle, eyes shouldn't compete with the mouth and the mouth shouldn't compete with the eyes."

"As for bridal hair, keep it simple and stick to what you've got. Don't go adding hair pieces in order to add height - it's too complicated and unless done professionally, can end up looking unnatural. Just keep it shiny and elegant."

COLOUR MATCH

Make-up artist Naveeda gives her guide on make-up colour choices that can work with your bridal outfits.

"As a general guideline, the colours you choose should work with your skin tone, as well as the shade of the outfit. Sometimes, contrasting hues can look fabulous too."

RED

Shades of red, rust and bronze are very complimentary. Duskier complexions can look gory with reds so try to stick with rusts and warmer tones to really bring out your skin colour. Fairer skins look lovely with dark brown, smoky eyes.

PINK AND CERISE

For brides wearing shades of pink, I would recommend steering clear of matching eyes. Contrasting colours such as aubergines and plums with touches of gold and soft pink work beautifully. Go for dusky or dolly pink on the lips.

WHITE OR GOLD

You can work with almost any colour. With white and gold dresses, I like to enhance the eyes with pinks and lilacs. Smoky brown eyes also work, as do charcoals. Opt for a lip colour to compliment your complexion. If you choose strong eyes, be sure to keep the lips neutral.

GREEN

Pistachio green teamed up with shades of bottle green gives the lids a beautiful contrast. It also gives the eyes amazing depth and really brings them out. Don't be afraid of using bright colours - a touch of vibrant eyeshadow can look really striking.

MAROON

Aubergine shades with complementing golds work really well with this colour. Dusky complexions should stick to soft golden tones, which can brighten up the skin. Splashes of deep maroon can do the same for fairer complexions. A hint of maroon dabbed on to the lips with a touch of gold highlighter at the centre can look very glamorous.

TURQUOISE

Give the eyes some depth by blending shades of navy with golds. If you can't carry heavy colours over the entire lid, add a stroke of liner from a shade in the blue colour family. For lips, pale and vibrant pinks can look very pretty. Avoid reds and maroons as these can give you an 'older-looking' appearance.

CHAPTER TWELVE
HENNA

HENNA

The source of henna, in wedding traditions, is hard to track due to centuries of migration and cultural interaction. Poetry, literature, mythology and paintings show that henna art was being used as long as 5000 years ago for both cosmetic and healing purposes.

The henna plant, Lawsonia inermis, is a flowering shrub that grows to a height of about ten to fifteen feet. It can be found in countries with hot climates like Egypt, India and Morocco. Henna leaves are dried and crushed into a bright green powder, then made into a paste using oils and tea.

The traditions in which henna is incorporated vary from culture to culture. The most popular traditions tend to be weddings and religious festivals such as Eid.

Henna for brides

The most popular occasion for henna use is the wedding ceremony and in Hindu, Muslim and Sikh marriages henna adornments are considered to bring good fortune. Traditional bridal designs tend to be very intricate and extremely detailed involving free-hand paisley shapes. Female friends and family members will get together at the 'mehndi night' to apply designs on the hands and feet of the bride-to-be. The henna is usually wrapped in linen and left on overnight to allow the stain to become as dark in colour as possible. It takes around 48 hours for colour to fully deepen and mature. Generally, heat generated through the body influences the depth of the colour and this can range from a bright red to brick red. Some even say that the darker the stain the more successful the marriage will be.

Did you know?

Traditionally the name or initials of the groom would be cleverly hidden and intertwined amongst the design and the bride would ask him to find it on their wedding night.

Henna for fashion

In recent years, henna has become popular all over the world, for use in creating the simplest and most natural temporary tattoos. For those looking to have a personalized, pattern on the body (often the arms, back, navel and ankles) a henna tattoo is a perfect temporary option. It can also be used to create intricate ethnic or contemporary designs and can be individualized further by using small diamante bindis or glitter gel. Once painted on the skin, the henna will stain the top layer and can last for up to three weeks. Since pop icons like Madonna began using it a few years ago it has become a hot fashion trend in the West.

Henna patterns and styles

In different cultures the style and patterns of traditional henna art can vary immensely. Mehndi designs in the subcontinent usually feature floral and paisley patterns, which are set to a reddish-brown tone all over the hands, forearms and feet. Traditional Arabic designs are usually larger floral patterns concentrated on the hands and feet. In Africa bolder, geometric designs are more common and appear mainly in black.

Henna for the hair

As a healing plant, henna has many therapeutic properties. It helps to condition, cleanse and cool the skin on the scalp. Women and men regularly apply henna to their hair, especially in the subcontinent where it aids in keeping the scalp cool during the hot summer months.

Mehndi-artist Ash Kumar says: "Henna can be applied to the hair with egg yoke which helps to condition as well as to relax, soothe and calm the scalp."

Henna is a coating dye and is popular for its hair-dying properties. When applied to the hair, it stains the outer layer. The intensity of staining depends on your hair's natural colour and porosity. Dark locks will usually turn to a warm red.

- The earliest historical documentation of henna are the traces found upon the nails of mummified pharaohs. Based upon that evidence and existing images, it is thought that henna was used as a 'royal manicure' in ancient Egypt to colour and condition the nails.

- It is believed, that the henna plant arrived in India as a gift from Egypt. There is much debate as to when it actually arrived on the subcontinent, and many say it was during the Moghul Empire.

- Henna is considered to be a herb that has long been known to posses healing qualities. In ancient times it was used to cure ailments such as headaches, stomach pains, burns, athlete's foot, and open wounds. Spiritually, henna is believed to bestow happiness, good fortune and all the compassion of the universe.

- In the Kamasutra, the epic Indian guide to love, women were advised to learn the arts of tattooing and of colouring their teeth, garments, hair, nails, and bodies with henna.

- In countries where henna is rooted in historical tradition, members of the working class more commonly apply it for medicinal and healing purposes. In Egypt, members of the working class would dip their hands and feet in henna to produce a solid covering.

- There is some linguistic speculation that the term 'hen party' is a shortening of the term henna party.

- Henna stains the nails with a deep colour that will remain until the nail grows out. It also improves the health and quality of the nails.

- Before modern applicators such as henna cones were invented, henna would be applied on the palms using twigs, then by toothpicks and in later years, hair pins.

How to make your own henna

There are many hundreds of recipes for creating henna paste. These differ across the world, and in some cases, families will have their own secret recipe, which has been closely guarded for generations.

Guinness World Record holder Ash Kumar lifts the lid on his own secret recipe

Ingredients:

1 tablespoon of powder per applicator (one applicator will cover one hand)
1/2 teaspoon of eucalyptus oil to every two tablespoons of powder
1/2 teaspoon of clove oil to every two tablespoons of powder

Method:

- Put the henna powder in a stainless steel or ceramic container.

- Add the eucalyptus and clove oil. (These work to improve the usability and staining ability of your mehndi.)

- Add cold water to the ingredients until the paste is neither too thick or too thin. A toothpaste-like consistency is ideal.

- Fill the applicator with the paste and your henna is now ready.

- Remember that good quality henna will stain your skin with colour within minutes of application.

- Smoothness and staining power really depends on the quality and brand of henna being used. Be sure to use henna powder that is designed for the body and not the hair.

- To make the colour appear deeper, brush a mixture of lemon juice and sugar on the design, before the henna is washed off.

CHAPTER THIRTEEN
BOLLYWOOD BEAUTY

BOLLYWOOD BEAUTY

A Bollywood movie serves up a stunning visual feast for the viewer. The breath-taking backdrops of a Swiss mountain, the ornate replication of a Mughal palace, the romantic stroll across Mumbai's Juhu Beach, are all beautiful settings that we have become familiar with. When you watch a Bollywood film you are transported to another world. Central to this fantasy is the leading lady. A Bollywood heroine may have the allure of a seductress or the innocence of a girl-next door, but one thing is for sure; she is always beautiful. And for as long as films have been popular, it is the actresses who have set the trends and inspired female film-fans all over the world.

Hindi film critic Saibal Chaterjee says: "Every female actor who has attained mass popularity has done so because she has had something unique to offer in terms of looks and appeal. Each era gets the stars it desires and the female stars, on their part, with the personas that they project on screen, define and fulfil the aspirations of lesser mortals. They become embodiments of the sort of beauty, sensuality and grace that both men and women fantasise about or aspire to."

The success of these romance-driven films rest solely on the answer to a filmmaker's eternal questions, will the masses fall for my leading lady? Can her beauty capture the hearts of a billion-strong audience?

If we look at how cinema has evolved in Bollywood, it is fascinating to see how beauty has adapted too. The make-up and hair-styling has changed through the decades and strongly defined the style of the time. Modern day make-up artists often revive these classic looks, and enjoy adding a contemporary twist.

MAKE-UP'S MAGICAL MOMENTS

1930's

Devika Rani is still remembered as the first lady of the Indian screen and was considered a great beauty. She was the only Indian actress ever to have gained rave reviews from the English press.

The Star newspaper, in London, once said of her: "You will never hear a lovelier voice or diction. Or see a lovelier face. Devika Rani is a singular beauty." The Manchester Daily Despatch said: "Devika is so lovely, she puts the stereotyped charms of Hollywood blondes completely in the shade."

Saibal Chaterjee says: "She defined the characteristics of the Hindi film heroine for subsequent decades, especially that of the rural belle, combining within her a quintessential Indianness and the uncomplicated yet assertive air of a free-spirited child of nature. Her beauty was therefore both spontaneous and cultivated."

Other female stars of the time included the fearless "Hunterwali" Nadia who was born in Australia to a Greek mother and an English father. The masses loved the brazen, gutsy image of a masked white woman who wore daring shorts and slinky tops in these ultra-conservative times.

Saibal says: "She presented a personification of the erotic male fantasy of a fair-skinned, skimpily-clad woman. She possessed a high degree of sexual allure which made Nadia one of the most intriguing embodiments of beauty that Hindi cinema has ever witnessed."

The make-up look at the time was very much similar to that of Hollywood. Hair was styled into defined and structured waves. The complexion was pale, almost porcelain-like. Eyebrows were plucked extremely thin and then re-drawn with a thin line. As for lips, red was the colour of the decade. Lips were outlined into a perfect 'cupid's bow' shaped using a lip pencil and filled in immaculately with lipstick.

Devika Rani

40's This was the era where glamour swept into Bollywood and was epitomised by Nargis, with her desirable natural beauty and magnetic screen presence. Suraiya also graced Hindi cinema screens in the '40s with a rare beauty and style that was seductive and bewitching. Perfect grooming was considered essential and women were no longer ashamed of wearing make-up or shorter hairstyles. Having perfectly roller-curled "Nargis-esque" hair was a statement of liberation for many women of the time. Eye make-up became a focus with more use of eyeshadows, pencils and mascara. The eyebrow shape also became noticeably heavier and lips were filled with rich, deep shades of colour.

153

Madhubala

Meena Kumari

50's

If Marilyn Monroe was the enduring Hollywood icon of the 1950s, Madhubala will forever be remembered as her Bollywood equivalent.

"There has been nobody quite like Madhubala, a sprightly seductress whose popularity hinged on her ineffable glamour and understated sex appeal," says Saibal Chatterjee.

Many say that Madhubala was without doubt the most beautiful Hindi film heroine ever with her dancing eyes and lopsided smile. Her beauty at times would attract more attention than her performances. She gave India an icon to love and served as a benchmark for future beauties. Meena Kumari and the southern belle Vyjayanthimala were also hailed as beauty icons of Bollywood's 'golden decade'. Meena Kumari captivated audiences with her soulful tear-laden eyes and Vyjayanthimala with her innocent beauty. Softly applied red lipstick was a key look for this era in shades of crimson, berry and ruby. Eye make-up was also a focus with lashings of mascara and false lashes. Subtly blushing cheeks completed the look.

154

Nutan

Asha Parekh

60's "This was the decade when fashion statements in films jumped out of the screen and influenced the masses for the first time. It was also a time when the concept of sheer entertainment became a reality in commercial Hindi cinema, and the screen beauties of the era reflected a footloose, fancy-free spirit," says Saibal.

Asha Parekh headlined the swinging '60s bombardment along with Sadhana, Saira Banu, Sharmila Tagore, Waheeda Rehman, and Nutan. The teenage Asha Parekh represented the new Indian youth with an East-meets-West fashion sense. Hairstyles in the '60s were completely different from the more formal styles of the '50s. Doll-like Sadhana started a craze for her Audrey Hepburn-inspired fringe, which came to be known as the "Sadhana cut". The style spread, making her the fashion legend of her age. This was also the rebellious years and Sharmila Tagore proved this in 1966 when she became the first heroine to pose in a bikini for a magazine spread. With her occasionally in-your-face sensuality and consistent elegance, Sharmila gave sex appeal a modern definition. She still remains one of India's leading exponents of style. And who can forget the high glamour quotient of the lovely Saira Banu, the classically pretty Waheeda Rehman and the exquisite beauty and grace of Nutan? These beauties were a part of a high gloss and high glamour era and together, they took Hindi cinema into a new age. "Their hair-dos, their dresses and their overall demeanour impacted street fashion, marking the beginning of a continual interrelationship between the style of the female stars and what their fans aped liberally," adds Saibal.

This was the decade where make-up became fun and the '60s was all about the eyes. Kohl was used to line and elongate the eyelids and thick, black 'winged' out liner was popular. Eyeshadow was used to exaggerate the sockets and fake lashes would dramatise the eyes even further. The use of blusher also became big news and lips remained almost nude, coral or clear to draw more attention to the eyes.

Sharmila Tagore

70's

Saibal says: "The concept of beauty underwent a dramatic change in Hindi cinema, flooded as it was during this decade with a bevy of sassy, sensual female stars who pushed the boundaries of sexual assertion further than ever before."

This was the decade of freedom and self-expression. For the first time taboo issues such as sex and drugs were depicted in films such as Hare Krishna Hare Ram and the look of many leading ladies reflected these changing times. Zeenat Aman, Parveen Babi, Hema Malini, Rekha, and Jaya Bhaduri were the leading heroines of the decade, each possessing a unique style of beauty. The former Miss India Zeenat Aman brought to Hindi cinema a fresh, sexy ensemble of pizzazz and sensuality. She constantly pushed the boundaries with her liberated attitude and revealing costumes, which gave her performances a sensual edge never before seen in a Bollywood actress. Parveen Babi was another star whose Westernized, femme fatale persona combined with sex appeal, seduced the Bollywood audiences. The sultry Rekha religiously followed a high maintenance beauty regime and in her time was India's ultimate and most glamorous cover girl. The wilder, liberated actresses contrasted with the decade's more traditional, simplistic beauties. Hema Malini's beauty captured the bohemian essence of the '70s. Her fans labelled her the 'dream girl' as her sheer beauty and screen presence held audiences captive. Subhash Ghai put it best when he said, "For 15 years, the whole of India went to the theatres just to see Hema - her smile, her warmth or just her."

Then there was Jaya Bhaduri whose dusky skin and simplistic girl-next-door beauty needed very little make-up to enhance.

"Watchers of popular Hindi films saw a balancing act unfold before them: on one hand were the seductresses such as Zeenat and Parveen who thrived on the art of titillation on the other were more traditional charmers like Hema and Jaya who worked their magic on the masses in subtler ways," says Saibal.

Hair in the '70s was hippy-like, long, free, flowing and centre-parted. Softly layered Farah Fawcett-style flicks were also common. Make-up was fresh faced with visible blusher, rainbow-coloured eyeshadow and plenty of lip gloss.

Sridevi

80's The most prominent leading lady of this decade was Sridevi, who conquered the silver screen with her huge saucer-like eyes and round face. Her reign at the top lasted almost ten years, largely because she was so versatile and could slip effortlessly into any role. Dimple Kapadia was also a beauty icon of the '80s who became an instant star with her almost casual sexiness and seductively falling voluminous hair. Big hair, with lots of volume, teamed up with vibrant lips created the trademark look for this era.

Aishwarya Rai

90's

The '90s saw a whole generation of gorgeous icons emerge. Madhuri Dixit was hailed as the most beautiful actress to have adorned the silver screen since Madhubala. After her "Ek do teen" number from her first hit movie Tezaab in the late '80s, Madhuri Mania swept Bollywood. Almost every man in the country fell in love with her blinding smile and overwhelming sex appeal. This was also the decade where the unconventional, effortlessly beautiful Kajol, charmed Bollywood and set new standards for 'natural` looking heroines. The enigmatic Manisha Koirola and glamorous Karisma Kapoor were also leading ladies of this era, but there was nobody who could truly rival Madhuri at the peak of her prowess.

Significantly, the mid '90s saw India enjoy an unprecedented run of success in international beauty pageants. It all began in 1994 with Sushmita Sen winning the Miss Universe title and Aishwarya Rai being crowned Miss World. Aishwarya captivated the Hindi film industry and audiences with her dazzling looks and doe-eyed innocence. Her beauty has made her one of India's first global brand-ambassadors, endorsing products for cosmetic giants such as L'Oreal.

In the '90s women embraced a minimalist 'no-make-up' look for the first time. Instead of being painted on, make-up was often used to enhance the heroine's natural beauty. Take a look at Kajol in Dilwale Dulhania Le Jayenge or Aishwarya in Taal, and you will see simple beauty personified. All the hair and make-up excess of the '80s, was abolished. In came straight, shiny hair with a more subtle approach to make-up.

Priyanka Chopra

Kareena Kapoor

OO's The two key words to describe this century are 'individualism' and 'choice'. The dramatic spurt in beauty queens and ramp models-turned-film heroines continues with stars such as Bipasha Basu, Lara Dutta and Priyanka Chopra, to name only a few. These beauties have established themselves as leading actresses and have in the process, strengthened the cult of flawless beauty. Bipasha Basu and Mallika Sherawat are constantly pushing new boundaries with their choice of daring roles and by embracing Westernized principles. Whereas Rani Mukherjee, the dusky Bengali beauty who is arguably the decade's number one actress, embodies the girl-next-door. Her natural acting ability and versatility has won her a legion of male and female fans. The ravishing Kareena Kapoor gives the traditional audiences the fair and lovely look India has always admired. Dimple-faced Preity Zinta is perhaps India's most contemporary actress. Her bright,

bubbly, cheeky image speaks directly to the country's ever-growing middle class. We also have Priyanka Chopra, who, in many ways, embodies the complete Indian heroine, as she is equally comfortable with the Western look as she is with the traditional.

The beauties of our decade have proved that there are no rules. Actresses and make-up artists are looking westwards for fashion and beauty influences. Make-up is being used to suit the individual beauty and character. Just look at how make-up artist Kapil Bhalla gave Bipasha a sexy kohl enhanced 'bird-eye' look in Jism and the way Mickey Contractor gave Preity Zinta the 'girl-next-door' look in Kal Ho Na Ho. Period films also give make-up artists and actresses a chance to experiment with looks and styles. For her role as a nineteenth century courtesan in The Rising, Rani Mukherjee smudged kohl on her eyes to replicate the charcoal used by, dancing girls of the era.

CHAPTER FOURTEEN
CATWALK SECRETS

CATWALK SECRETS

When you see a good fashion show, it's a slick and polished affair, looking almost effortless in its presentation. But this is not the case behind the scenes, as a dedicated team of dressers, runners, hair-stylists and, of course, make-up artists clamour to create a visual feast. The dressing area can get pretty hectic with models vying for mirror space and make-up artists adding their last minute beautifying touches. But beneath the chaos, it's dedicated professionalism and skill that ensures the models look their very best as they walk down the ramp. These pages are your backstage pass where some of the industry's top insiders expose their secrets on how they get the girls to look so stunning and some of your favourite models share their beauty must-haves.

Red lips can work on any skin tone, just balance them with a fresh complexion. Use a sheer foundation and go easy on the blusher. If full on red is too harsh for you, dab on the colour with your fingers.

Stylish hair needs the correct tools. Straightening-addicts should steer clear of irons with metal plates. Go for a ceramic model, which distributes heat more evenly. A flat, wide paddle brush is best for smooth and straight styles.

Add intensity to the eyes with lashings of volumising mascara and some individual lashes. Pat on some nude gloss to the middle of the lips to add fullness.

"NARS Body Oil is perfect for showing off a well toned body. It gives a beautiful healthy glow."
Clint Fernandes - Make-up artist

"Soft and dewy skin is the most complementing texture for the face. For dusky beauties like Carol Gracias and Nina Manuel,
I like to blend liquid bronzer, foundation and cream blush together to achieve a very dewy, shimmery look."
Mehera Khola - Make-up artist

For a sexy and flawless back - exfoliate, moisturise and use a body foundation or concealer to disguise blemishes.

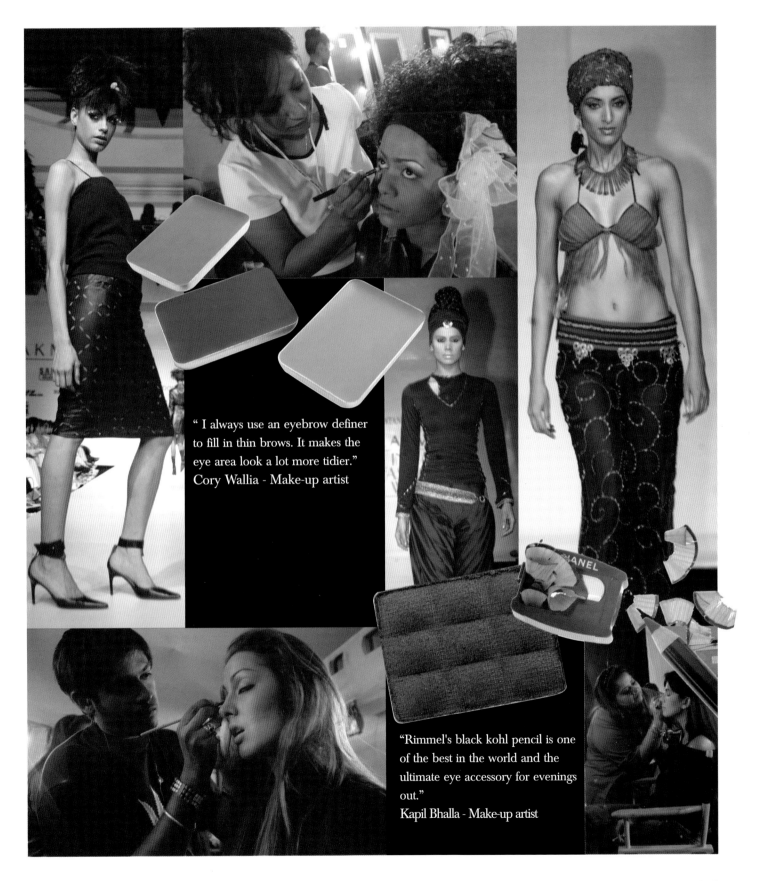

" I always use an eyebrow definer to fill in thin brows. It makes the eye area look a lot more tidier."
Cory Wallia - Make-up artist

"Rimmel's black kohl pencil is one of the best in the world and the ultimate eye accessory for evenings out."
Kapil Bhalla - Make-up artist

"Evian Mineral Water Spray is great for freshening and hydrating the skin in between shows, when the make-up is starting to feel heavy."
Joey Matthews - Model

"The night before a show I apply La Prairie Under Eye Gel and Skin Caviar. I wake up with skin that is supple and fresh with no puffiness."
Vidisha Pavate - Model

"Just before make-up application, I apply MAC Strobe Cream on my face. It helps the base to sit well on the skin and adds a fantastic glow."
Shamita Singha - Model

"I always carry my La Prairie Make-Up Remover, Evian Water Spray and some cotton swabs to every show. I prefer the fresh, natural 'no make-up look' so I like to remove it all after the show."
Carol Gracias - Model

"My favourite backstage product is MAC Fix+ - I use it before applying foundation and after moisturizer. It tightens the pores, helps the base to stay on for longer and gives a smooth, long lasting appearance."
Tapur Chatterjee - Model

"I am big fan of Clarins products - I especially love their eye creams and Beauty Flash Balm - it instantly wakes up my skin."
Dipannita Sharma - Model

"I love using MAC Bronzing Powder on Carol Gracias - it gives her dusky complexion an even glow. It works so beautifully that I don't even need to use any foundation or concealer."
Clint Fernandes - Make-up artist

"It is important to highlight and shade for the catwalk. However, each model needs a particular direction and trick and it is important to know what you want to hide or highlight!"
Jojo - Make-up artist

"To dusky skin a stunning glow - my secret weapon is liquid Metallizer (in bronze) by Make Up For Ever. I blend it into foundation for a wonderful flush of bronze."
Cory Wallia - Make-up artist

"Two products I cannot do without is my mascara and eyelash curlers - they are super essential for livening up and transforming the eye area. My top beauty tip is to thoroughly moisturise the face before applying make-up."
Nina Manuel - Model

168

CHAPTER FIFTEEN
BODY AND MIND

AYURVEDA

Ayurveda is the ancient medical science that originated over 5,000 years ago and has grown into a respected and widely used system of healing. The word is derived from the Sanskrit word Ayur meaning life and Veda meaning science.

Bharti Vyas says: "Science of life means that the internal environment of the body is very much affected by the food we eat, the environment we live in and the thoughts we have. These are all the things that releases the body's own chemicals, which could have an effect on imbalancing the functioning of the vital organs."

At the heart of Ayurveda lies the fundamental principle that the body and mind are connected. In other words, the body affects the mind and the mind affects the body - the two are forever intertwined. Due to this connection, in Ayurveda there is no such thing as a purely physical or psychological ailment. In understanding this relationship we can seek happiness on the outside by working on the inside.

If you can incorporate Ayurvedic principles of wellbeing into your life, you can appear happier, healthier and ultimately more beautiful.

Replace disorder with calmness and chaos with serenity around you and this will help restore your body's natural balance. This is what Ayurveda teaches us. Yoga, meditation and massage are all cornerstones of living a life in accordance with Ayurvedic beliefs.

CHAKRAS AND DOSHAS

In Ayurveda it is believed that there are seven chakras, which are all interconnected. When the chakras are in balance, the physical, mental and spiritual aspect of 'self ' reaches a state of harmony, contributing to your overall health and wellbeing. Chakras run from the bottom of your spine up to the top of your head. Both, yoga and meditation can help to keep the chakras in balance. Ayurveda's principles lay with the idea of three doshas or 'life forces' which are Kapha (earth and water), Pitta (fire) and Vata (air) these three must be kept in harmony for a healthy, happy and long life.

We all have three doshas within us. However, one or two of these will be predominant. When the three are disturbed it can cause illness and deterioration of the body. An ayurvedic practitioner looks to balance the doshas.

Each dosha has certain tendancies:
Vata: If you're a Vata, you tend to be very creative and good at linking concepts and communicating inspiration. You are easily anxious, quick to learn, but easily forget. You also often expect the worst.

Pitta: The pitta mind is a collector of information, you are quick thinking, intelligent and organised. You are determined to succeed and driven by ambition.

Kapha: You have a steady mind that can focus on a wide number of issues at one time. Your memory is excellent and you tend to remember the smallest details. Loyalty to friends and a stable and regular environment is also important to you.

Ayurvedic treatments and massage

Massage can help keep the body balanced and centred. It boosts circulation to bring more nutrition to the cells helping to remove metabolic wastes and toxins that can build up in your body. Specific oils work to align each dosha.

Here are a few of the main Ayurvedic treatments

Oleation is a treatment that uses friction massage with blended essential oils (similar to an aromatherapy massage).

Panchakarma, meaning five actions is a deep cleansing, purification treatment that uses essential oils, massage and meditation techniques to drive out excess doshas and toxins from its cells.

Shirodhara involves slowly pouring warm herb-infused oil over the middle of the forehead, where the Ajna (third eye) exists. It induces total relaxation.

Siddha Vaidya is a medical discipline based on the five senses, or elements, which correspond to earth, water, fire, air, and ether (space). Only plants and plant-based derivatives are used in the treatment against dosha imbalances because of their inherent purity.

Nasaya is a nasal oil drop treatment and is great for relieving discomfort in the neck, shoulders and head as well as congestion, sinusitis and puffy eyes.

COLLECTION OF MEDICINAL PLANTS

Five ways to bring Ayurveda into your lifestyle

1 Take regular walks. In Ayurveda, walking is regarded as a simple, strain-free exercise that balances the doshas.

2 Eat fresh foods every day. Processed foods are tougher to digest and offer little of nature's benefits.

3 Drink plenty of water. Water is nature's great healer. It aids digestion and banishes toxins.

4 Disconnect from the outer world and give yourself some 'me time'. Sit comfortably and close your eyes in a peaceful environment, which will help beat stress and accumulate positive energy.

5 Phone a friend. People who make us happy, are like medicine. Nurture your heart by staying in touch with loved ones.

Did you know?

Ayurvedic Tales

A common tale from ancient Indian folklore recalls how around 3,000 years ago, a group of fifty-two holy men left their homes and went to live in the foothills of the Himalayas. They were in search of a cure for the ailments that had been plaguing human beings for centuries.

Little did they know that their quest would pioneer one of the oldest, most consistent and time-tested disciplines of science in the world, Ayurveda.

These holy men, known as Rishis, became the first physicians of humanity. Their body of knowledge was not committed to writing, but was passed from generation to generation by word of mouth.

YOGA

Yoga is considered to be the oldest physical discipline in existence. The word yoga is derived from the Sanskrit word yuj meaning to yoke or bind and is often interpreted as 'union'. The ultimate aim of yoga is to strike a balance between mind and body and attain self-enlightenment. To achieve this, yoga uses a combination of movement, breathing, posture, relaxation and meditation.

Yoga has been continuously evolving since its inception thousands of years ago. Even though universally perceived as a perfect antidote to the vagaries of modern day physical and mental stress and ailments, it has over the years, come to acquire various forms and meanings for different people. Today many of the original 'yoga' practices have been altered and adapted to fit into current day lifestyles. However, despite the changes, the essence of yoga and its ultimate goal has remained the same - assisting us to achieve the optimum level of physical, mental and spiritual well-being.

Nearly all yoga styles are rooted in Hatha yoga; a physical discipline that focuses on developing control of the body through asana (posture). It is the yoga of physical well-being. While all styles seek to balance the body, mind and spirit, they go about it in various ways. They may differ in how asana are done and where they focus the attention (on mastering and holding the posture, on strict alignment, on breathing or on the flow of movement). Some will use props for the asana; others will crank up the temperature in the room. No style is better than the other; it is a simple matter of personal preference.

Did you know?

The Indian sage Patanjali is believed to have collated the practice of yoga into the Yoga Sutra an estimated 2,000 years ago. The Sutra is a collection of 195 statements that serves as a philosophical guidebook for most of the yoga that is practiced today.

ESSENTIAL YOGA TIPS

· The ideal time to practise yoga is in the morning before breakfast, when the mind is calm and body movements can be performed with ease and vitality.

· Choose a place that is free from distraction. A peaceful, and quiet environment is essential.

· Begin with easy poses and then proceed to the tougher ones. Remember that being methodical and systematic is the key. If you begin to feel tired inbetween, you should discontinue.

· Yoga clothing should be loose and as comfortable as possible.

· While performing yoga, your breathing should be long and deep. Keep your mouth closed and inhale and exhale only through the nose.

MEDITATION

There are many different types of meditation but one definition that covers all is a state in which the body is consciously relaxed and the mind is allowed to become calm and focused. Meditation allows you to consciously direct your attention to alter your state of consciousness. During meditation, people often direct their attention towards various things such as symbols, colours, uplifting thoughts, sounds, or chants. It has been used for decades as a means of spiritual growth.

In recent years, meditation has become a valuable tool for us in our demanding and fast paced world. It allows us to find a peaceful oasis, to let go of stress, daily pressures and negativity.

MEDITATION TIPS

· Leave your expectations aside and remember that there are is no fixed criteria for determining successful meditation.

· Try not to over analyse the meditation or put too much emphasis on doing it right. Meditation is only difficult if we become too concerned with doing it correctly. Staying focused does become easier with time and practice.

· Find a quiet, comfortable place to meditate. You can sit on a chair, on your bed, or on the floor. You don't necessarily have to sit cross-legged.

· When meditating, make sure you sit comfortably with your spine reasonably straight. This allows the spiritual energy to flow freely up the spine, which is an important aspect of meditation.

· Eliminate as much noise and distractions as possible. But, don't worry about things that you cannot control.

INNER BEAUTY

We all know that make-up, hair colour and clothes make us look good on the outside. However making our 'inner selves` feel good is just as important.

We can feel beautiful by developing self-esteem and radiating confidence. If you follow steps to better yourself from the inside it will reflect on the outside to those around you - it's the kind of beauty you just can't buy in a bottle. Positive thinking leads to a positive aura, which can leave its mark on the people we meet. Remember, you live with yourself 24 hours a day, seven days a week, so make sure you are happy with the person you are.

10 steps to inner beauty

Best-selling author and life coach Robin Sharma offers his exclusive tips on how to feel good internally.

1 Eat a superb diet

You become what you eat. You wouldn't put low-grade petrol in a Ferrari, so why put poor foods into your body? Eating more fruits, vegetables, less meat and doing proper supplementation with vitamins will promote beauty and good health.

2 Spend time in silence

In the East, the sages used to say "Silence is nature's sweet restorer." Being silent for even 15 minutes a day leads to a much better experience of life. And when you feel less stress and more joy, your appearance improves.

3 Exercise regularly

In my book The Monk Who Sold His Ferrari I share many powerful ideas that have helped so many people live better lives. One simple idea I share is the importance of putting your health as your number one priority. Exercising brings energy, stamina and beauty.

4 Think good thoughts

Human beings can control their thinking. Thinking thoughts that are inspiring and positive brings inner peace. And inner peace leads to outer beauty.

5 Have a weekly massage

Commit to a weekly massage. Not only is it incredibly relaxing, it keeps you healthy and leads to a glowing complexion.

6 Find work you love

Life is too short to do work that you dislike. Have the courage to do work that uplifts you and makes you happy.

7 Commune with nature

No matter how busy my life gets, I find time each week to spend in nature. It renews me. It relaxes me. It rejuvenates me- inside and out.

8 Clear out anger

Anger leads to a whole host of adverse health effects. Use tools like journalling and meditation to process through anger. You will feel lighter. You will look better.

9 Associate with great people

I joke with my audiences that "You become who you have lunch with." We become who we speak to. Associate with excellent people and your life becomes excellent.

10 Take regular vacations

Vacations are not a waste of time. They renew and refresh you. They keep you interested in life. They help you stay energised. Vacations keep you at your best. And living at your best is a key purpose of life.

TRADITIONAL BEAUTY REMEDIES

Head massage

Champi or head massage is an ancient technique that has played an important part in Indian life for nearly 4,000 years. Today, everyone from children to grandparents use the technique to relieve stress, improve overall health and promote healthy hair growth. South Asian women all over the world use it as part of their regular grooming routine. Vegetable oils such as coconut, olive, almond, and sesame are used to nourish the hair and promote circulation through scalp massage. Not only will massage work wonders for your hair but if you are feeling tense and under pressure it is great for relieving accumulated tension. The variety of massage movements that are used can help to reduce stress, fatigue, increase mental clarity and rejuvenate the mind.

Benefits of scalp massage

A weekly warm oil massage can be beneficial in many ways.

• It helps to prevent dry and flaky scalp conditions without the use of harsh chemical shampoos.

• It helps stimulate blood circulation in the head and neck area. When the scalp is tight from stress and tension, circulation and hair growth are obstructed.

• It helps strengthen the roots and nourishes the hair shaft, promoting new growth and strengthening current hair.

• By softening and conditioning the hair it makes it more manageable.

• Massage enables the natural oils to spread evenly along the hair instead of remaining at the roots. This will improve overall lustre and vibrancy.

• Hair is very delicate and should be handled with care. Massage the scalp gently, using the fingertips in small circular movements.

Massaging with appropriate oils can enhance the experience and improve results.

Almond oil is very nourishing for the scalp and hair. Its moisturizing properties can help reduce scalp stiffness and tightness.

Sesame oil is beneficial in the treatment of dandruff. It also prevents premature greying and promotes growth.

Coconut oil is cooling and can help reduce hair problems such as thinning.

Olive oil has great purifying properties.

Brahmi oil helps calm the mind and nervous system and is very nourishing for the hair, helping to promote thickness.

Amalaki oil is cooling, nourishing and purifying all at the same time, so it is ideal for all types of hair.

Hibiscus oil helps maintain hair colour and vitality.

Neem oil has purifying and cleansing properties.

DIY BEAUTY

Homemade products are a great way to give the skin an indulgent treat. They are also packed with fresh and natural ingredients, which are free from additives and preservatives. Create your own using a few simple ingredients.

Nourishing mask for dry skin

Mix together: One egg yolk, a teaspoon of honey, a teaspoon of olive oil and a teaspoon of vitamin E oil. Spread the mix over the face and neck. Leave on for 15-30 minutes then rinse with lukewarm water. Honey is a natural humectant, which means it has the ability to attract and retain moisture.

Balancing mask for oily skin

Spoon out half a grapefruit and squeeze the juice from half a lemon. Put both in a blender and add two egg whites. Throw in a generous handful of seedless grapes. Blend the ingredients together. Apply to the face and leave for 15 minutes, then rinse off with warm water. The grapefruit unclogs pores, lemon is an excellent astringent and the egg whites work to tighten the skin.

Strawberry mask for radiance

Using a fork, mash eight or nine strawberries into a paste-like texture. Add three tablespoons of honey and mix. Apply directly to the skin and leave for two minutes before rinsing with plenty of water. Strawberries are rich in vitamin C, but make sure you are not allergic to them.

Milk and honey rinse for wrinkled skin

Add one tablespoon of raw honey, 125ml of milk and one teaspoon of aloe vera gel to a jar and shake well. Apply to your face morning and evening with a cotton ball. As skin ages, it loses its ability to retain water, becomes dry and appears wrinkled. Milk contains lactic acid, which is an alpha hydroxy acid that helps to cleanse and exfoliate the deepest layers of the skin.

Detoxifying papaya body scrub

Peel and crush a whole papaya, then mix with some jojoba seeds, grated orange peel and two drops of grapefruit essential oil. Scrub all over the body before showering. The jojoba seeds and orange peel works to remove dead skin cells and stimulate the circulation, while vitamin A rich papaya accelerates the formation of new skin cells.

Warming ginger and lemon body scrub

Mix together a handful of sea salts with some almond oil and a few drops of lemongrass and ginger essential oils. Use all over the body before a bath or shower. Dead skin cells will be eliminated and the lemongrass and ginger aroma will leave you uplifted with a feeling of warmth.

Storage: Most recipes require refrigeration since they do not contain preservatives. Packed in air-tight glass container, they will stay fresh for approximately one-two weeks.

BODY BEAUTIFUL

Get scrubbing

To maintain a smooth-as-silk canvas exfoliation is key. Not only does it give the complexion a glow by shedding dead cells, it also minimises the appearance of pores, reduces ingrown hairs and allows moisturising products to penetrate better. Polish your body in circular movements twice a week using a gentle daily exfoliator - the skin will look dramatically smoother.

Boost moisture

Moisturise your body at least once a day with a cream that is suitable for your skin. Avoid mineral oil-based creams as they can be heavy and greasy and don't absorb well. They can also promote dehydration when used long term.

Eliminate stretch marks

Stretch marks are tiny tears in the dermis, experts believe that if the skin is kept soft and supple it is less likely to tear. Stretch marks can occur after dramatic weight loss or after giving birth. Unfortunately, once they have turned a silvery-white colour there's not much that can be done to remove them. If they are a reddish-purple tone then retinoid creams such as Retin-A or Renova can help to lighten their appearance. Laser treatment is another option, but it is costly and regular maintenance is required. If you're prone to stretch marks, massage areas of concern daily, with a easily absorbed body oil. You can also cover any imperfections with a body foundation.

Blemish free back

A spotty back is caused by inflammation of the sebaceous glands (the glands that produce oil). Some of the factors that can trigger it include hormonal changes, too much fat and sugar in the diet and stress. The back area is hard to reach and usually covered with clothes therefore it's often neglected, but it is important to include it in your beauty regime. Keep the back area clean - dermatologists suggest washing it with a cleanser containing salicylic acid. Be extra gentle when cleaning the area, as aggressive actions can strip the skin of its natural protection and leave it vulnerable to bacteria.

Don't pick at spots and always gently pat the area dry or if possible allow it to dry naturally after a bath or shower. If the acne is severe, see your doctor who may prescribe a stronger topical lotion or suggest laser treatment.

Cellulite

Cellulite can be a sign of poor circulation, imbalanced hormones, a bad diet or lack of exercise. Because it has so many triggers, it can be difficult to treat. Cellulite is most common on the bottom, thighs and knees, but can also be found on the stomach and back of the arms.

How to banish it

Exercise

Any form of exercise, from brisk walking to swimming to yoga can assists the circulation and firm the muscles.

Diet

A diet rich in high fibre, fresh fruits and vegetables is recommended. Reduce your intake of sugar, alcohol, caffeine, dairy products and red meat as they are harder for the body to eliminate. Drink plenty of water - one or two litres a day will help flush out nasty toxins and waste.

Reduce stress

A build up of tension blocks the tissues, preventing waste elimination. Relaxation and deep breathing exercises will help to ease tension and oxygenate the body.

Dry skin brushing

This is one of the cheapest and most effective ways of stimulating the circulation. Just five minutes of body brushing before showering, can make a huge difference. Invest in a natural bristled brush. Use it in long, brisk strokes from the ends of your arms and legs toward lymphatic drainage 'hubs' like the underarms, inner thighs, and backs of knees. Brush firmly and concentrate on the worst patches of cellulite. This invigorating process helps to speed up the flow of your lymph as well as shedding dead cells.

Massage

Massage target areas that are difficult to stimulate with good old exercise. Beauty guru Bharti Vyas says: "Use the balls of your fingers in small circular movements to massage the entire body, then pinch the skin using all four fingers and thumb - this combination will help to stimulate the lymph systems, increase circulation and eliminate waste." For faster action, gently massage in an anti-cellulite cream or oil to problem areas. When it comes to products, don't expect miracles, but if your regime is disciplined and the product is applied daily, the active ingredients can certainly help.

ADDRESS BOOK

GLOBAL BEAUTY DIRECTORY

Jet setters, make sure you look and feel your best wherever you are in the world. Here's a guide to the best salons and spas across the globe.

AUSTRALIA

ADELAIDE

Amista Hair Body & Face
187 Payneham Road
St Peters
Tel: +61 08 8362 8663

Axia
234 Rundle Street
Tel: +61 08 8223 4636

Browns Hairdressers
101 Gilbert St
Tel: +61 08 8212 4101

Essential Beauty
Regent Arcade
Shop 4a Rundle Mall
Tel: +61 08 8232 2225

Exotic Hair & Beauty Centre
Shop 10 Rundall Mall
Adelaide Central Plaza
Tel: +61 08 8232 6066

Hair & Beauty With Attitude
191 O'Connell Street
North Adelaide
Tel: +61 08 8267 2969

MELBOURNE

35th Avenue Designers In
Hair & Beauty Therapy
35 Massey Avenue
Reservoir
Victoria. 3073
Tel: +61 03 9469 5279

D & D Hair & Body
Shop 18/ Meadow Heights
Shopping Centre
Paringa Boulevard
Meadow HeightsVictoria 3048
Tel: +61 03 9309 9077

Human Nature
604 Hampton Street
Brighton Victoria 3186
Tel: +61 03 9553 8777

SYDNEY

Ella Rouge
Westfield Sydney Central Plaza
Shop LG 15 Central Plaza
450 George Street NSW 2000
Tel: +61 02 9239 0800

Fascination Beauty Salon
186 McElhone Street
Kings Cross NSW 2011
Tel: +61 02 9357 237

Fusion Hair & Body
Level 9 Phillip Street
Hotel Intercontinental
NSW 2000
Tel: +61 02 9247 2083

Halt Hair & Beauty
32-40 Halt Street
Surry Hills NSW 2010
Tel: +61 02 8399 0141

Philippe Xavier Hairdressers
4 Bridge Street NSW 2000
Tel: +61 02 9247 7077

CANADA

OTTAWA

Baz Beauty Solutions
146 Colonnade Road
Nepean ON K2E 7Y1
Tel: +1 613 723 3159

Beauty Studio
1896 Prince of Wales Drive
Nepean ON K2C 3W9
Tel: +1 613 225 8803

Enviro Trends Pure & Natural Beauty
1642 Merivale Road
Nepean ON K2G 4A1
Tel: +1 613 727 2676

Madison's Studio Spa
1234 Merivale Road ON
K2C 4C3
Tel: +1 613 715 9614

Paddy Beauty Salon
RM 209-Carlingwood
Shopping CentreON K2A 1S3
Tel: +1 613 725 1582

Riverside Mall Beauty Salon
735 Ridgewood Avenue
ON K1V 6M8
Tel: +1 613 733 3344

Studio Elegante
1370 Clyde Avenue
Nepean ON K2G 3H8
Tel: +1 613 224 6771

Sass Hair
1489 Merivale Road
Nepean ON K2E 5P3
Tel: +1 613 225 3332

Vanity Hair Tanning & Beauty Salon
117 Centrepointe Drive
Nepean ON K2G 5X3
Tel: +1 613 225 8583

VANCOUVER

Fern's Day Spa
4185 Main Street BC V5V 3P6
Tel: +1 604 874 8623

Forever Young Beauty Centre
3344 Cambie Street
BC V5Z 2W5
Tel: +1 604 877 1323

New Capital Beauty Hair Salon
3702 Main Street BC V5V 3N7
Tel: +1 604 873 9063

La Maine Beauty Salon
4536 Main Street BC V5V 3R5
Tel: +1 604 327 7919

Lisa Beauty Center
3021 Cambie Street
BC V5Z 4N2
Tel: +1 604 876 6431

Romance Beauty & Hair Salon
3482 Main Street BC V5V 3N2
Tel: +1 604 873 9890

TORONTO

Annie's Beauty Lounge
2499 Yonge Street
ON M4P 2H6
Tel: +1 416 488 9141

Armond Beauty Salon
2588 A Yonge
ON M4P 2J4
Tel: +1 416 322 4884

Beauty Exchange Inc
3281 Yonge Street
ON M4N 2L8
Tel: +1 416 932 2445

Beauty Village Spa Inc
2287 Yonge Street
ON M4P 2C6
Tel: +1 416 483 8065

Beauty World
2510 Yonge Street
ON M4P 2H7
Tel: +1 416 486 0322

Brookdale Beauty Salon
1A Brookdale Avenue
ON M5M 1P2
Tel: +1 416 489 5260

Nasrin Hair & Beauty
2481 Yonge Street
ON M4P 2H6
Tel: +1 416 485 2225

Vivian's Beauty Spa
2628 Yonge Street
ON M4P 2J4
Tel: +1 416 932 8036

UNITED KINGDOM

LONDON

North London

Ash Kumar Henna Artist
149 Princes Avenue NW9
Tel: +44 0 20 8204 7771

Beauty Care
438 Muswell Hill Broadway N10
Tel: +44 0 20 8444 5982

Crown Academy of Hair Extensions
15 High Street HA9
Tel: +44 0 20 8795 5001

Hamstead Garden Beauty Salon
32 The Market Place NW11
Tel: +44 0 20 8731 7311

Henna Artisan
Flat 4 Downing Court N12
Tel: +44 0 20 8492 1961

Hena Hair Beauty
324 Regents Park Road N3
Tel: +44 0 20 8349 9911

La Mirage Beauty & Laser Clinic
632-640 Kingsbury Road NW9
Tel: +44 0 7956 325222

Nila's Hair & Beauty
722 Kenton Road HA3
Tel: +44 0 20 8204 1144

Pamela Stevens Beauty Clinic
948 Green Lanes N21
Tel: +44 0 208 360 3108

Samira Hair & Beauty
78 High Street HA8
Tel: + 44 0 20 8951 3463

Shila's Hair & Beauty
371 Fore Street N9
Tel: + 44 0 20 8803 7550

Uma Hair & Beauty Centre
233 Hertford Road N9
Tel: +44 0 20 8350 5404

East London

Amina's Hair & Beauty
3 Eustace Road E6
Tel: + 44 0 20 8548 4969

Beauty at Anju's
390 Green Street E13
Tel: +44 020 8586 9679

Elegant Hair & Beauty
164 Church Road E12
Tel: + 44 020 8478 3800

Geetha Designer Hair & Beauty Salon
31 Plashet Grove E6
Tel: +44 0 20 8470 1776

Hair & Beauty by Kanwal
147 Green Street E7
Tel: +44 0 20 8548 8842

Jags Hair & Beauty Salon
314 Ilford Lane IG1
Tel: +44 0 20 8514 4499

Joshiv Beauty International
Studio C and D
11 Burford Road E15
Tel: + 44 0 8704 450 022

Neelam's Hair & Beauty
161 Green Street E7
Tel: +44 0 20 8552 8008

Yasmins
227 Green Street E7
Tel: +44 0 20 8552 1200

Zeenat
172 Green Street E7
Tel: +44 0 20 8821 9999

Zeenat Al Nisad
64 Green Street E7
Tel: +44 0 20 8257 0007

West London

Aasia Khan
136a Tweed Court
Hanway Road W7
Tel: +44 0 20 8231 1817

Ginger Group House of Hair & Beauty
43 High Street W5
Tel: +44 0 20 8567 5264

Kavita's Beauty Parlour
Gladstone Cottage
Wimborne Avenue UB2
Tel: +44 0 20 8813 8777

Neelam Beauty
129a Ealing Road HA0
Tel: +44 0 20 8903 2163

Oasis Beauty Clinic
231-233 Greenford Road
UB6
Tel: +44 0 20 8578 8989

Pari Beauty Parlour
131 Ealing Road HA0
Tel: +44 0 20 8903 0870

Ritz Herbals Beauty Salon
37 South Road UB1
Tel: +44 0 20 8571 5788

Shahnaz Herbal Beauty
115-119 The Broadway UB1
Tel: +44 0 20 8574 4488

Shringar Mood
101 The Broadway UB1
Tel: +44 0 20 8571 2020

Simi's Health & Beauty Salon
3 Leeland Road W13
Tel: +44 0 20 8810 1927

Varsha Hair & Beauty
5 Holly Avenue HA7
Tel: +44 0 20 8206 2616

Virinder Saini Beauty Clinic
256 Ealing Road HA0
Tel: +44 0 20 8903 9626

Zaynab - The Beauty Co
428 Rayners Lane HA5
Tel: +44 0 20 84261808

South London

Beauty Haven
97 Norfolk Avenue CR2
Tel: +44 0 20 8657 5445

Dimple's Beauty
54 Upper Tooting Road SW17
Tel: +44 0 20 8767 4444

Karismah Beauty
262a Brixton Hill SW2
Tel: +44 0 20 8671 4287

Revive Beauty Salon
57 Tooting High Street SW17
Tel: +44 0 20 8682 4209

Sajna
234a Upper Tooting Road
SW17
Tel: +44 0 20 8767 9191

Central London

Agua Spa @ The Sanderson
Sanderson Hotel
50 Berners Street W1T
Tel: +44 0 20 7300 1414

Aveda
174 High Holborn WC1V
Tel: +44 0 20 7759 7355

Bharti Vyas Holistic Therapy
24 Chiltern Street W1U
Tel: +44 0 20 7486 7167

Bliss Spa
60 Sloane Avenue SW3
Tel: +44 0 20 7590 1790

Clarins Studio at Fenwick
63 New Bond Street
W1S
Tel: +44 0 20 7493 1901

Charles Worthington (hair)
7 Percy Street W1T
Tel: +44 0 20 7631 1370

Daniel Galvin (hair)
58-60 George Street
W1U
Tel: +44 0 20 7486 9661

Elemis Day Spa
2-3 Lancashire Court W1S
Tel: +44 0 20 8909 5060

Hari's (hair)
305 Brompton Road SW3
Tel: +44 0 20 7581 5211

The Janet Ginnings Hair & Beauty Salon
45 Curzon Street W1
Tel: +44 0 20 7499 1904

Martyn Maxey (hair)
18 Grosvenor Street W1K
Tel: +44 0 20 7629 6161

Nyumba House of Hair & Beauty
Mount Street W1K
Tel: +44 0 20 7408 1489

Philip Kingsley Trichological Clinic
54 Green Street W1Y
Tel: +44 0 20 7629 4004

Richard Ward Hair & Metro Spa
82 Duke of York Square
SW3
Tel: +44 0 20 7245 5161

Saks Hair & Beauty
4-10 Tower Street WC2H
Tel: +44 0 20 7379 1188

The Sanctuary Spa
12 Floral Street
Covent Garden
WC2E
Tel: +44 0870 770 3350

Shenaz Shariff at The Face and Body Clinic
57 Harley Street
W1G
Tel: +44 0 20 7436 3936

Spa Illuminata
63 South Audley Street
W1K
Tel: +44 0 20 7499 7777

SPA NK
127-131 Westbourne Grove
W2
Tel: +44 0 20 7727 8002

Trevor Sorbie (hair)
27 Floral Street
WC2E
Tel: +44 0 20 7379 6901

Urban Retreat at Harrods
87 Brompton Road SW1X
Tel: +44 0 20 7893 8333

Vaishaly Facialist Clinic
51 Paddington Street
W1U
Tel: +44 0 20 7224 608

BIRMINGHAM

Alishas Beauty Box
674 Coventry Road
Small Heath B10
Tel: +44 0 121 773 5870

B Beautiful
234 Soho Road B21
Tel: +44 0 121 551 7503

Beauty
Hyatt Regency Hotel
2 Bridge Street B1
Tel: +44 0 121632 1690

Beauty Above
8 Solihull LaneB28
Tel: +44 0 121744 9197

Beaute Academy
48 Frances Road
Lozells
B19
Tel: +44 0800 001 5329

The Beauty Clinic
4C Heathfield Road
Kings Heath
B14
Tel: +44 0 121694 4145

Beauty at Ethos
42 Hollywood Lane
Hollywood
B47
Tel: +44 0 121430 3969

Beauty Works
29 Formans Road
B11
Tel: +44 0 121 778 6555

Body and Being
Canal Square
Browning Street
B16
Tel: +44 0 121 456 7633

Elegant Beauty
386 Stratford Road
Sparkhill
B11
Tel: +44 0 121 783 1207

SK:N
Lasercare
86 Bull Street
B4
Tel: +44 0 121 237 2040

BRADFORD

Beauty Box
82 Toller Lane BD8
Tel: + 44 0 1274 492963

The Beauty Clinic
2 Napier Terrace
Leeds Road BD3
Tel: +44 0 1274 656556

The Beauty Studio
360 Otley Road BD2
Tel: +44 0 1274 633309

Hair & Body Tree
10 North Parade BD1
Tel: +44 0 1274 721133

KD Electrolysis
24 Cross Street
Reading RG1
Tel: +44 0 118 956 7720

Style & Profile
Unit 1 Walsh House
Rawson Place BD1
Tel: +44 0 1274 728430

Sweet & Simple
11 Upper Millergate
BD1
Tel: +44 0 1274 723659

LEEDS

The Beauty Crescent
12 The Crescent LS6
Tel: +44 0 113 289 9122

Clarins Studio
Harvey Nichols
107-111 Victoria Quarter
LS1
Tel: +44 0 113 242 4282

Distinctive
Beauty
15-19 Cowper Road
LS9
Tel: +44 0 113 240 2240

Eternal Beauty
33 Compton Road
LS9
Tel: +44 0 113 249 9777

Major Hair & Beauty Co
The Balcony
64 Merrion Centre
LS2
Tel: +44 0 113 245 8281

Mint Nail & Beauty Bar
16 Boar Lane
LS1
Tel: +44 0 113 242 8811

Pro-Style Hair &
Beauty Salon
12-14 Market Street Arcade
LS1
Tel: +44 0 113 245 0288

Saks Hair & Beauty
Units 3-5 Queens Arcade
LS1
Tel: +44 0 113 246 7666

Skin Deep Beauty
Salon
84 Otley Road
LS6
Tel: +44 0 113 275 1715

Woodhouse Health &
Beauty Clinic
2 Woodhouse Cliff
LS6
Tel: +44 0 113 275 3692

LEICESTERSHIRE

Beauty Lounge
63 Main Street
LE5
Tel: +44 0 116 246 1175

Beauty Sanctuary
45 Belvoir Street
LE1
Tel: +44 0 116 285 5638

Beauty Zone
67 Evington Road LE2
Tel: +44 0 116 285 6699

Bliss Beauty Salon
A/66 Catherine Street
LE4
Tel: +44 0 116 266 8561

Body Bliss
50d Blaby Road
South Wigston LE18
Tel: +44 0 116 278 9293

Chakra
Stretton Court
Stretton Road
Great Glen LE8
Tel: +44 0 116 259 0123

Clarins Studio
The Shires Centre
20 St. Peters Lane
LE1
Tel: +44 0 116 251 6462

Gabbi
176 Fosse Road North
LE3
Tel: +44 0116 251 6476

Jaimini Beauty Clinic
67 St. Saviours Road
LE5
Tel: +44 0 116 249 0619

Jazz Beauty
7 Parkstone Road
LE5
Tel: +44 0 116 241 3322

Krystal Clear Beauty
279 Melton Road
LE4
Tel: +44 0 116 266 0616

MANCHESTER

Asian Creations
1 Bramley Avenue M19
Tel: +44 0 161 257 3658

Clarins Studio
Kendals Deansgate M3
Tel: +44 0 161 831 9902

**Elegant Nail &
Beauty Salon**
271 Abbey Hey Lane M18
Tel: +44 0 161 292 2220

Finesse
10-14 Hilton Street M1
Tel: +44 0 161 236 1401

Jesshalia Hair & Beauty
97 Claremont Road
M14
Tel: +44 0 161 342 0000

Re-Nu
Top Floor
93a Princess Street M1
Tel: +44 0 161 228 6902

**The Royal Exchange
Beauty Spa**
19 Royal Exchange Arcade
M2
Tel: +44 0 161 834 5959

Samia's Beauty Spot
123 Manchester Road
M21
Tel: +44 0 161 860 4200

**Sahara Hair & Beauty
Parlour**
428 Cheetham Hill Road
M8 9LE
Tel: +44 0 161 795 6385

INDIA

MUMBAI

Ayush Therapy Centre
Shop No 7 Ground Floor
Royal Sands
Andheri-Link Road
Tel: +91 22 26347534

b:blunt
Ground floor Kohinoor Bldg
29 Hughes Road
Tel: +91 22 55880370

**Bennys Beauty &
Hair Care**
1F Juhu Supreme Shopping
Centre JVPD
Tel: +91 22 26209616

Biotique
10 Khatu Mansion
Warden Road
Tel: +91 22 23635844

Bharat & Dorris
Near Juhu Centaur Hotel
Juhu Tara Road
Juhu
Tel: + 91 22 26192886

2c/4 Poonam Vihar
Poonam Nagar
Mahakali Caves Road
Andheri East
Tel: +91 22 28364697

Shop 184
First Floor City Mall
Adlabs
Oshiwara
New Link Road
Andheri West
Tel: +91 22 56987088

Clarins Beauty Studio
White Hall
143 August Kranti Marg
August Kranti Road
Tel: +91 22 23643685

Champagne
2-3 Imperial Plaza
30th Road
Bandra West
Tel: +91 22 26400400

Chi-Kaba
4 Mangal Smruti
Khar
Tel: +91 22 26049610

Dilshad's Salon
Nav Pooja Apartments
11-A Perry Cross Road
Bandra West
Tel: +91 22 26431770

Freeda
41 Pali Hill Road
Bandra West
Tel: 91 22 26486321

**Faridas Avanti
Beauty Clinic**
60 Hill Road Bandra West
Tel: +91 22 26406293

Finesse
2 Shiv Darshan Building
33 Road
Bandra
Tel: +91 22 6400659

**Habibs Hair &
Beauty Salon**
Shoppers Stop
S.V Marg
Kandivli
Tel: +91 22 28076566

Shoppers Stop
211-D S.V Road
Andheri West
Tel: +91 22 26240451

Shoppers Stop
Nirmal Lifestyles
L.B.S. Marg
Mulund West
Tel: +91 22 25935023

Shoppers Stop
Flat No. 1406/28A
Link Road
Malad West
Tel: +91 22 56434726

Shoppers Stop
Linking Road
Bandra
Tel: +91 22 56017692

Hazel Beauty Salon
23 Juhu Supreme
9th Gulmohar Cross Road
Juhu
Tel: +91 22 26208199

**Headliners Hair &
Beauty Clinic**
109 Avon Arcade
D J Road
Vile Parle West
Tel: +91 22 26123491

HFX
98 Hill Road Bandra West
Tel: +91 22 26427672

Innovative Cure
B/7 Asha Colony
Opposite Sea Princess
Juhu Tara Road
Juhu
Tel: +91 22 26607609

Jacques Dessange
The Taj Mahal Hotel
Colaba
Tel: +91 22 56653366

Jiva Spa
Taj Hotel & Palace
Apollo Bunder
Colaba
Tel: +91 22 5665 3366

Juice
The Courtyard
41/44 Minoo Desai Marg
Colaba
Tel: +91 22 56385488

JW Marriott
Juhu Tara Road
Juhu Beach
Tel: +91 22 56933000

Kaya Skin Clinic
1st Floor
Waterfield Road
Bandra West
Tel: +91 22 26424586
To locate your nearest clinic
log onto
www.kayaclinic.com

Lakme
Beauty Salon
2/B Industrial Assurance
Building
Opposite Eros Cinema
J Tata Road
Churchgate
Tel: +91 22 22042104

Kailash Shop
1 Ground Floor
156 Waterfield Road
Bandra West
Tel: +91 22 26421410

3 Arsiwala Building
61 Nathalal
Parekh Marg
Wodehouse Road
Colaba
Tel: +91 22 22181747
To locate your nearest salon
log onto
www.lakmeindia.com

Lubu's Salon
8 Shantivanam
34-B Pali Road
Bandra West
Tel: +91 22 26406290

MAC
Dynamix Mall
Juhu Scheme
Tel: + 91 22 2670 5603

Dynamix Mall
Sant Dhyaneshwar Marg
JVPD
Vile Parle
Tel: + 91 22 2670 5603

Mane Event
Shop No. 1
Chetak Society
41 Palli Hill
Bandra West
Tel: +91 22 2607241

Nail Bar
Grace Classic
Ground Floor
14th Road
Khar
Tel: +91 22 55838464

Nalini & Yasmin
Sagar Fortune 2nd Floor
Waterfield Road
Tel: +91 22 56680089

Pooja Apartments
2-3 17th Road Khar
Tel: +91 22 6484445

39 Sun N Sand Hotel
Juhu
Tel: +91 22 6242988

Redz Oxygen
Bar and Salon
25H Sea Palace
Shop No 8
Juhu Tara Road
Juhu
Tel: + 91 22 56992420

Salon Simone
Jewel Arcade 1st Floor
Waterfield Road
Bandra West
Tel: + 91 22 26435668

Sarla's Cosmetic
& Laser Clinic
1 Manokamana
210 T. H. Kataria Marg
Mahim West
Tel: +91 22 24459009

Scissors Over Comb
Samudra Mahal Worli
Tel: +91 22 24966118

Serena's Beauty Saloon
Sankal Building
Ground Floor
Turner Road
Bandra West
Tel: +91 22 26424210

Serena's Beauty Salon
Astoria Hotel
Room No. 508
5th Floor Churchgate
Tel: +91 22 22820485

Schnell Hans
International
111/112 Mistry Chambers
1st Floor Colaba
Tel: +91 22 22832499

Shahnaz Husain Herbal
Shahnaz Herbals
Maker Arcade
Cuffe Parade Colaba
Tel: +91 22 22185325

Sheetal Beauty Parlour
28/A Kamdhenu
Shopping Centre
Lokhandwala Complex
Andheri West
Tel: +91 22 26320406

Silhouette
Hotel Oberoi Towers
Nariman Point
Tel: +91 22 22029963

Taj Land Stand
Beauty Salon
Band Stand Bandra West
Tel: +91 22 56681234

NEW DELHI

Aaina Beauty Parlour
C-4E/ 335 Janak Puri
Tel: +91 11 25528704

Asian Roots
B-5/15 Safdarjung Enclave
(Opp. DLTA and Deer Park)
Tel: +91 11 51651010

Beyond Looks
12 Pal Mohan Apts
Club Road Punjabi Bagh
Tel: +91 11 26449992

Classic Beauty Clinic
A-1/113
Lajpat Nagar-1
Tel: +91 11 6836783

Delhi Electrolysis and Beauty Clinic
40 Hanuman Road
Connaught Place
Tel: +91 11 23362093

Habibs
M-3 Ground Floor
South Extension
Part II
Tel:
+91 11 26252727

F-38 South Extension
Part I
Tel: +91 11 51646150

9/10 East Patel Nagar
Tel: +91 11 52481727

32 North West Avenue
Club Road
Punjabi Bagh
Tel:
+91 11 25167761

AM-34
Shalimar Bagh
Tel: +91 11 27488026

Kritika's Beauty Parlour
23/2 East Patel Nagar
Tel: +91 11 52481499

Lakme
Beauty Salon
Preet Vihar-100
New Rajdhani Enclave
Tel:
+91 11 22027001

Madonna
45 Basant lok
Vasant Vihar
Tel: +91 11 26145704/2818.

HS 37
Kailash Colony Market
Tel: +91 11 26145704

Noorjehan Beauty Parlour
The Claridges Hotel
12 Aurangzeb Road
Tel: +91 11 23010211

Hotel Oberoi
Zakir Hussain Marg
Tel: +91 11 26837278

Reflexions
Salon
C-197 First Floor
Greater Kailash Part I
Tel: +91 11 6485512

Step-In Beauty Parlour
F-14/55
Model Town 2
Tel: +91 11 7427242

Surya Beauty Parlour
Site-1392
Vikaspuri
Tel: +91 11 5506963

Vandana Luthra Curls & Curves
A-1/29
Main Najafgarh Road
Janakpuri
Tel: +91 11 5500608
Log onto
www.vlcc.co.in
for your nearest salon

BANGALORE

Bounce
First Floor Magnolia
Vittal Mallya Road
Tel +94 80 4132-9100

Cut & Color
G-1 Sai Villa
Wood Street
(opp Brigade Towers)
Tel: +94 80 2556-3546

Exclamation
First Floor
No 3047
80 Feet Road
HAL 2nd Stage
Tel +94 80 41154949

F Salon
Le Meridien
Sankey Road
Tel +94 80 2226-2233

Fussion
73/1 Nandidurg Road
Chingappa Garden
Link Road
Tel: +94 80 23335610

Jiva Spa
Kuteeram
Rural District
Karnataka
Tel: +94 80 28466326

No 66 Residency Road
Karnataka
Tel: +91 80 56604545

Limelite
554 10th A Main Road
5th Block Jayanagar
Tel +91 80 2521 1672

Lips - Stitch
579 20th Main
8th Block
Koramangala
Tel +91 80 2571 0653

Mirrors and Within
The Oberoi
37-39
Mahatma Gandhi Road
Tel: +91 80 2558 5858

Neeru's
25 Gurappa Avenue
Primerose Road
Tel: +91 80 2558 0880

Priti's Beauty Parlour
3 Anjaneya Complex
Airport Road
Tel: +91 80 2527 5209

Salon Squeeze
No 71 Ground Floor
2nd Cross
Lavelle Road
Tel: +91 80 4112 1220

Soul Beauty Salon
5 Ground Floor
2nd Cross
Vasanthnagar
Tel: +91 80 2235 0983

Spratt
The Hair Studio
Marielle Appartment
3 Magrath Road
Tel: +91 80 2509 1110

The Taj Beauty Parlour & Barber Shop
Taj Residency
41/3 Mahatma Gandhi Road
Tel +91 80 5660 4444

CHENNAI

Anushka Unisex Hair & Skin Salon
6 Thyagaraya Road T. Nagar
Tel: +91 44 5217 9197

Beaubelle Beauty Salon
KHEC Towers
42 1st Main Road
C.I.T. Nagar West
Nandanam
Tel +91 44 24312015

Bounce
123 Ispahani Centre
Nungambakkam High Road
Tel: +91 44 2833 0508

Bright Beauty Parlour
83 Mudichur Road
Tel: +91 44 2226 2568

Cuts & Curls
20 Taylors Road
Kilpauk
Tel: +91 44 4217 8042

Fair 'N' Lovely L'oreal Prestige Salon
First Floor R A Puram
3rd Cross Street
Tel: +91 44 2435 2809

Jiva Spa
Fisherman's Cove
Covelong Beach
Kanchipuram District
Tel: +91 44 6741 3333

Naturals
No 37 First Floor
Sona Bulidings
C.P Ramaswamy Road
Tel: +91 44 5519 5851

KOLKATA

Habib's Hair & Beauty Studio
8 Ho Chi Minh Sarani
Tel: +91 33 2282 6317

June Tomkyns
26 Ballygunge Circular Road
Suite 3
First Floor
Tel: +91 33 2475 7025

L'Oreal Collaboration Family Salon
The Enclave
7/1F Alipore Road
Second Floor
Tel: +91 33 2448 9424

Orchid Ladies Beauty Parlour
850 Lake Town
Jessore Road
Tel: +91 33 2334 2833

Rapunzel
Himadri
22 Ballygunge Park Road
Tel: +91 33 2405 137

Saajo Ladies Health and Beauty Clinic
40/1A Bhupen Bose Avenue
Tel: +91 33 2555 4278

Silhouette
The Oberoi Grand
15 Jawaharlal Nehru Road
Tel: +91 33 2492 323

Taj Bengal Beauty Salon
24B Belvedre Road
Tel: +91 33 2233 939

Urvashi Ladies Beauty Parlour
Rm1/26 Behala Comm Complex
Tel: +91 33 2468 4275

GOA

Goretti's Beauty Parlour
Monteiro Vaddo
Utorda
Majorda
Tel: +91 832 2754634

Head Lines Beauty Salon
6 Model's Residency
St Inez
St Inez Road
Tel: +91 832 2422801

Jiva Spa at Taj Exotica
Clawaddo
Benaulim Salcete
Tel: +91 832 2771234

Sereno Spa at The Park Hyatt
Arossim Beach
Cansaulim
Tel: +91 832 2721234

Shahnaz Husain's Herbal
Dt-8 Pancharatna Complex
Margao
Tel: +91 832 2715036

Shalaka Beauty Parlour
51 Kamat Arcade Street
Inez Panaji
Tel: +91 832 2452118

Spa at the Leela
Mobor
Cavelossim Salcete
Tel: +91 832 2871234

Sweety Beauty Parlour
Flat No 1
First Floor Shambhavi
Appartments
Dr D V Road
Panjim
Tel: +91 832 2230521

The Look Hair and Beauty Salon
Josyln Apts Rajwado
Mapusa
Tel: +91 832 2250861

KERALA

Divya The Health Spa
The Leela
Kovalam Beach
Trivandrum
Tel: +91 471 248 0101

Good Look Beauty Clinic
Vattolipady Jn
Iringole
P.O. Perumbavoor
Kochi
Tel: +91 484 2520577

Orchids Herbal Beauty Parlour
Angamaly JJ Towers
Railway Station Jn
Angamaly
Tel: +91 484 2455491

Swanys Beauty Parlour
Kadavanthra
Kochi
Tel: +91 484 2324499

Smart Look Beauty Parlour
Palarivattom
Kochi
Tel: +91 484 2335222

**Slimace Slimming and
Beauty Clinic**
G-87
Panampilly Nagar Kochi
Tel: +91 484 2323888

**Santhitheeram Holistic
Health Centre**
Koombayil Panangad P.O.
Ernakulam District
Tel: +91 484 3093220

Shahnaz Husain's Herbal
Hotel Abad Building
Chullikal Junction
Kochi
Tel: +91 484 2226414

**Somatheeram Ayurvedic
Beach Resort**
Chowara P.O
South of Kovalam
Trivandrum
Tel: +91 471 2266501

Wella Beauty Parlour
Ebenezer House
Beerankunju Road
Ernakulam
Tel: +91 484 2369938

**Women's World Beauty
Parlour & Health Club**
35/1453 Palarivattom
Kochi-25
Tel: +91 484 2349294

PAKISTAN

ISLAMABAD

Al-Saleem Beauty Parlour
1 Kohsar Market F-6/3
F-6
Tel: +92 51 2823940

Aslam Hair Dressing
Basement Harold's
International Store
School Road F-7
F-8
Tel: +92 51 2651080

Depilex
H. No 9B
Street 32
F-8/1
Tel: +92 51 2851647

Milli
H. No. 1
Street 9 F-7/3
Tel: +92 51 2651388

Moods
Street 42 F-8/1
F-8
Tel: +92 51 2852780

**Sufi Hair Dresser &
Beauty Parlour**
Shop 6 Block 7
Civic Centre F-7
Tel: +92 51 2827880

LAHORE

Alle Nora
86-B-II
Gulberg III
Tel: +92 42 5713686

Beauty Care Ladies Salon
6-A/C-II
M.M. Alam Road Gulberg
Tel: +92 42 6660920

**Beauty Care
Ladies Salon II**
35 Boulevard Cavalry Ground
Tel: +92 42 6660920

Depilex Beauty Clinic
14-C-1 M.M.
Alam Road
Gulberg 3
Tel: +92 42 5761080

**Dreamland Beauty
Parlour & Hair Stylist**
22-Bhandara Centre
138 Ferozepur Road
Tel: +92 42 758052

**Misbah's Skin,
Hair and Beautycare**
230-Y
Defence PH-11
Tel: +92 42 5723930

Nabila's Salon
11-C
Main Gulberg
Jail Road
Tel: +92 42 587 2546

**Nadira's
Beauty Parlor**
67-B-1
Near Sur Syed Road
Gulberg III
Tel: +92 42 5764925

New Look
7-C II M.M. Alam Road
Gulberg III
Tel: +92 42 5755070

Palpitations
14-C-II
Gulberg III
Tel: +92 42 5715414

Passion Looks
11-A Hali Road
Gulberg-II
Tel: +92 42 877646

KARACHI

**A.U. Beauty Parlour &
Training Institute**
A-24 Shalimar Bungalows
Block-17
Gulistan-e-Jauhar
Tel: + 92 21 8114935

**Azra's Hair &
Beauty Salon**
101 Sea Crest Phase-V
Khayaban-e-Shamsheer
Defence
Tel: +92 21 5854953

Bano Beauty Parlour
Near United Bakery
Allama Iqbal Road
Tariq Road
Tel: +91 21 4554898

**Bhabi's Health &
Beauty Clinic**
39 N.K.C.H. Society
Tariq Road
Tel: +91 21 4559191

Bina Beauty Parlour
N/E/11/13 Main Road
Nazimabad
Tel: +91 21 6683161

**Change Skin
Care Centre**
43/10/F
Block-6
PECHS
Tel: +91 21 4541836

Chic Beauty Palour
317-Allama Iqbal Road
1st Floor
PECHS
Tel: +91 21 4384433

G Squared @
Soma Hair Studio
360 6th Street
San Francisco
CA 94103
Tel: +1 415 861 4247

Hair Play
1599 Dolores St
San Francisco
CA 94110
Tel: +1 415 550 1656

Irina's Skin Care
29 Evelyn Way
San Francisco
CA 94127
Tel: +1 415 242 1023

Kamalaspa
7th Floor
240 Stockton Street
San Francisco
CA 94108
Tel: +1 415 217 7700

Neeta's Herbal
245 N Mountain Ave
Upland
CA 91786
Tel: +1 909 981 8004

Skin Deep -
The Body Spa
7862 Warner Ave
Suite J
Huntington Beach
CA 92647 Tel: +1 714 841 3313

Sublime Salon
2536 California St
San Francisco
CA 94115
Tel: +1 415 4404 920

Top Look
827 Sacramento St
San Francisco
CA 94108
Tel: +1 415 788 8818

Vinita's
11333 183rd Street
Cerritos
CA 90703
Tel: +1 562 402 1133

Zensasian
1311 23rd Ave
San Francisco
CA 94122
Tel: +1 415 682 8833

NEW YORK

Aaina
Beauty Salon
337 South Broadway
Hicksville
NY 11801
Tel: + 1 516 933 3524

Allure Day Spa
& Hair Design
139 E
55th Street
NY 10022
Tel: +1 212 644-5500

Aveda Aroma
Therapy Esthetique
509 Madison Avenue
NY 10022
Tel: +1 212 832 2416

Bliss 49
541 Lexington Avenue
NY 10022
Tel:
+1 212 219 8970

Christine Chin Spa
79 Rivington Street
NY 10002
Tel: +1 212 353-0503

Elizabeth Arden
Red Door Salon
691 Fifth Avenue
54th Street
NY 10022
Tel: +1 212 546 0200

Estee Lauder Spa
1000 3rd Avenue
NY 10022
Tel: +1 212 980 9040

Euphoria Spa
18 Harrison Street
NY 10013
Tel: +1 212 925 5925

Evolution Salon
20807 35th Avenue
Bayside
NY 1136
Tel: +1 718 229 8551

Frederic Fekkai (hair)
15 East 57th Street
NY 10019
Tel: +1 212 753 9500

Hinna
Beauty Salon
2-71 Main Street
Flushing
NY 11355
Tel: +1 718 460 9484

La Prairie at the
Ritz-Carlton Spa
50 Central Park Street
NY 10019
Tel: +1 212 521 6135

Neelu's Khubsoorat
43-10 Main Street
Flushing
NY 11355
Tel: +1 718 353 5089

Ohm Spa
260 5th Ave
7th Floor
Bet 28th &
29th Streets
NY 10001
Tel: +1 866 322 6155

Shobha's Hair &
Beauty Salon
8359 264th Street
Glen Oaks
NY 11004
Tel: +1 718 962 2895

Spa at Mandarin
Oriental
80 Columbus Cross
35th Floor
NY 10023
Tel: +1 212 805-8800

Sweet Lily
Natural Nail Spa
222 West Broadway
NY 10013
Tel: +1 212 925-5441

W Hotel Spa At
W New York Hotel
541 Lexington Ave
NY 10022
Tel: =1 212 407 2970

Vidal Sassoon
(hair)
767 5th Avenue
NY
Tel: +1 212 535 9200

MEET THE EXPERTS

MEET THE EXPERTS

The following people have contributed to this book with their expert knowledge and exclusive tips. They truly are the beauty 'insiders' and leading authorities in their fields.

Adhuna Bhabhani-Akhtar

Few people in India's hair industry have the profile or achievements to match Adhuna's. With a track record that stretches over 20 years, Adhuna trained in the UK where she worked for hair giants Wella. She then settled in India and joined the L'Oreal artistic team where she went on to win the L'Oreal Colour Trophy. Adhuna is regarded as one of India's leading hair stylists. She owns the b:blunt hair salon whose celebrity clients include Hrithik Roshan, Sameera Reddy, Aamir Khan, Arjun Rampal, and Preity Zinta. She has worked on various magazines, TV shows and Bollywood hits.

Ananda in the Himalayas

Nestled in the foothills of the Himalayas this award winning spa is a haven of healing. Its in-house team of ayurvedic doctors, therapists and yoga gurus are the best in the business. Whether your goal is stress management, deep relaxation, anti-ageing, beauty, detoxification or cleansing, the team at Ananda can help you rediscover tranquility and attain true wellness.

Asgar

Top hairstylist Asgar has been in the industry for over 20 years. Throughout his career Asgar has styled the tresses of the rich and famous. He is currently a Senior Stylist at one of London's most prestigious hair salons, Daniel Galvin. His amazing creativity is called upon for major fashion shows and editorial, fashion and beauty shoots. His work has graced the pages of international fashion bibles such as Vogue, Tatler, Marie Claire and Elle and newspapers including The Daily Telegraph, The Times and The Guardian.

Ash Kumar

The world's leading mehndi artist Ash Kumar has achieved international recognition as an icon in henna. His sheer speed has gained him a place in the Guinness Book of World Records as the "World's Fastest Henna Artist." His list of celebrity clients, span the showbiz world of Hollywood and Bollywood and he has worked his art on Julia Roberts, Rani Mukerjee, Kareena Kapoor and Salman Khan. His work has also been featured in many Bollywood blockbusters including Devdas and Hum Tum.

Aysha

Aysha began her career as a bridal make-up artist at the age of 17. Soon after she was signed up by MAC, where she now works as a senior artist at the UK's biggest counter in London's Selfridges. She has built up an impressive reputation amongst both customers and colleagues and is regarded as an expert on Asian bridal make-up and skin tones. Aysha also runs regular workshops on make-up and is a regular contributor at fashion shows and magazine editorials.

Bastien Gonzalez

Bastien is a trained podiatrist and has worked in some of the worlds most exclusive hotels - in Paris, London and New York. His unique medical pedicure has won him an A-list clientele. Those who are patient enough to wait months for an appointment with the man they call the 'foot-guru' won't be disappointed. Bastien also runs his own society where he selects and trains young pedicurists. His product line 'Révérence de Bastien' is fast becoming a sought after range.

Bharti Vyas

Bharti Vyas's innovations have been instrumental in helping to change the public's attitude towards health and beauty, and in the past two decades, she has altered the face of the beauty therapy industry. Bharti has been a practising holistic beauty therapist for the past 25 years. She is also a qualified aromatherapist, acupuncturist, ayurvedic wellbeing therapist, magnet therapist, and laser therapist. She regularly conducts seminars all over the world and her Skin Wisdom product range is sold in the UK's largest supermarket chain. Bharti is also author of seven books including Beauty Wisdom, Simply Radiant and Simply Ayurveda.

Clint Fernandes

Clint has been in the make-up industry for the past ten years during which his skills have taken him on various international assignments. His fresh, modern style has enabled him to work with some of India's top photographers, designers and models. His portfolio includes adverts for the likes of Lakme, Veet, Pepsi, Nokia and many more. Clint has also worked on almost every Indian supermodel and on memorable 'item numbers' such as the 'Babuji' song (in the film Dum) with Yana Gupta.

Cory Wallia

There are not many faces Cory has not worked on during his 15 years in the beauty business. He has worked his magic on top actresses and supermodels, including Madhu Sapre, Lisa Ray, Sheetal Mallar, Aishwarya Rai, and Malaika Arora Khan. Cory is highly respected amongst his peers and has become a sought after name in the business of beauty. Apart from innumerable commercials and ad campaigns, he is the man often called upon to forecast the ramp looks for Lakmé India Fashion Week as well as Lakmé's beauty looks for the coming season.

Dar

In a career spanning over 25 years, Dar has become an enormously successful hairdresser. He has worked in some of London's top salons including Vidal Sassoon, Michael John, before setting up his own highly renowned salon where he built up an international clientele of the rich and famous. Dar has worked on shoots for leading fashion magazines such as British and Italian Vogue, Tatler, and Cosmopolitan. It's celebrity clients include Yasmin Le Bon, Goldie Hawn, Imran Khan and Aishwarya Rai. He is currently based between Hari's salon in Chelsea and has his own salon in Delhi.

Dilshad Pastakia

Dilshad stands amongst the top hair stylists in India. She trained in Hong Kong and at London's Vidal Sassoon. She now owns her own salon and her client base ranges from young girls, housewives, working women to the crème-de-la-crème of society. She also has an impressive list of famous clients such as Shah Rukh Khan, Bipasha Basu, Rani Mukherjee, Upen Patel, and Mallika Sherawat.

Farah Naz

Farah is an associate of the Royal College of Science in London and has a degree in Biochemistry. She launched her own company, EX1 Cosmetics in 2003. Her vision was to develop a range of affordable cosmetics with premium performance for women of Far Eastern exotic skin tones. The EX1 range of foundations and powders are becoming widely available around the UK.

Jojo

Jojo trained in London and began his career in Mumbai. He was besed in Greece and Paris for a while where he further developed his skills and worked with some of the biggest names in fashion. In India, he is recognized as a top make-up artist, hair stylist and image consultant. He works primarily on fashion shows, advertising films, press ads, fashion and beauty features, exclusive brides, and editorials. He also conducts make-up and hair workshops.

The Kaya Skin Clinic

Kaya has over 42 clinics across India and Dubai. The objective of the clinics are to provide result-oriented, non-surgical skin solutions. The solutions available provide benefits such as, skin brightening and polishing, permanent hair reduction, pigmentation and acne scar reduction and age control solutions. These international skin solutions are offered in a serene environment to a clientele of over 75,000. All services are designed by a team of over 100 dermatologists.

Kapil Bhalla

Based in India, Kapil has worked his magic on India's leading supermodels and actresses, including Bipasha Basu, Shilpa Shetty and Mandira Bedi. He is also a make-up consultant for Indian cosmetic brand Lakmé and has worked on advertising campaigns for the likes of Ponds and Fair & Lovely. He has worked on fashion shows for almost every top designer in India and created genre-defining looks on movies such as Jism, Rog and No Entry.

Ketan Patel

Award winning Ketan Patel has won the ultimate industry accolade of Nail Technician Winner of Winners title from 1996 to 2001 throughout the professional nail show competition circuit. He is such a pro that he was banned from the arena at the end of 2001 as no one could beat him! He now runs the Creative Nail Academy in London. Ketan writes for both consumer and trade press and teaches competition style nail techniques to professional nail technicians wishing to emulate his incredible style.

Leena Jotangia

Leena is currently a well-respected part of the beauty team at the NARS counter in Manchester's Selfridges. She advises women of all skin complexions and textures on a daily basis and has worked on various fashion shows including the Clothes Show Live.

Mehera Khola

Mehera is a make-up artist and hair-stylist who has worked on international advertising campaigns for several years. Her celebrity portfolio includes the likes of Christina Aguilera and countless Bollywood heroines including Esha Deol in the movie Dhoom and Katrina Kaif in Maine Pyaar Kyu Kiya. Mehera regularly travels world-wide to work on bridal clients and is called upon to work on shows with top Indian designers including Manish Malhotra, Wendell Rodricks and Rocky S.

Mickey Contractor

With an impressive 26 years in the make-up industry, Mickey is amongst the make-up world's elite artists. He is the king of Bollywood make-up and has worked on almost every top actress including Aishwarya Rai, Rani Mukherjee, Kajol, and Sushmita Sen, to name but a few. His ad campaigns include Lux, Whirlpool, Tag Heuer and Coca Cola. Films include a list of blockbusters including Dil To Pagal Hai, Kuch Kuch Hota Hai, Kabhi Khushi Kabhie Gham, Chalte Chalte, Mohabbatein, Kal Ho Na Ho and Taal. Mickey has recently joined forces with MAC India as Director of Make-Up Artistry.

Nabila

Make-up artist, beautician and stylist, Nabila is a well-known name in Pakistan. The former model has been in the business for over 20 years with a beauty salon in Lahore and Karachi. She has diversified into image consultancy and her clientele includes many prominent Pakistanis. From designers Rizwan Beig, Sana Safinaz to photographers, Tapu Javeri, Khawar Riat to models Iraj, Amna Haq, to film stars Babra Sharif, and Reema - all have Nabila's number on their speed dial. She also owns a chain of nail bars in Pakistan called Nail Express.

Naveeda

Naveeda is a professional make-up artist and fully qualified beauty therapist. Her name has quickly become associated with innovation, style and above all satisfaction. With over seven years of experience in the highly competitive bridal make-up and commercial fashion industries in Britain, Naveeda has quickly established herself as an individual who is highly sought after. She is a regular contributor to leading Asian bridal and fashion bibles such as Asiana and Asiana Wedding.

Nina Haider

Nina is a fully certified hair and make-up artist and has spent over ten years perfecting her trade. Throughout her career she has worked for cosmetic houses including Estee Lauder, L'Oreal, Christian Dior, and Chanel. Her work has taken her to shoots all over the world and she has worked on major advertising campaigns for Marks & Spencer and Radox. Nina regularly works on fashion shows for leading designers in London and is considered to be a pioneer of make-up looks.

Pamie Dhanoa

Having suffered excessive hair growth throughout her life, Pamie spent years researching every medical resource she could find, and trying virtually all hair removal methods available. In 1997 she began to practice electrolysis and has since opened her own clinic. She has a huge client list and spends each day helping women to tackle excessive hair growth and feel more confident about themselves.

Patricia Akaba

Patricia Akaba has been in the hair extensions business for over 15 years. She teaches hairdressers the art of hair extensions and is an expert in all application methods. She has a loyal celebrity clientele and is a regularly contributes to television shows and magazine editorials.

Dr. Philip Kingsley

Dr. Philip Kingsley has trichological clinics in London and New York and a client list that includes celebrities, politicians and royalty. He is known in the field as the 'hair doctor' and is widely recognized as the leading authority on his subject. He is also author of the number one selling book, The Hair Bible.

Pooja Arora

Pooja is quickly establishing a name for herself in the Indian beauty world. She has worked on numerous magazine shoots for L'Officiel, Elle, Seventeen, Femina, New Woman, Verve, Cosmopolitan, Indiawali Bride and Femina Girl. She has also worked on campaigns including Pantaloons and Globus. She has transformed a number of models and actresses including Mallika Sherawat, Malaika Arora Khan, Riya Sen, Madhu Sapre, Ujjwala Raut, and Nina Manuel with her fresh style.

Robin Sharma

Robin is the author of seven international bestsellers including the inspirational book The Monk Who Sold His Ferrari. He is one of the world's top experts on leadership, elite performance and personal growth. His ideas on self-mastery and organizational excellence have helped millions of people in over 35 countries and companies like FedEx, Nike, IBM, General Motors, and Panasonic. A well-known speaker, he frequently shares the stage with individuals such as Bill Clinton, Ken Blanchard, Jack Welch, and Deepak Chopra.

Ruby Hammer

Internationally acclaimed make-up artist Ruby Hammer has worked with cosmetic houses including Estee Lauder, Clinique, Christian Dior, Clarins and Revlon. Leading publicaions constantly call upon Ruby's extensive knowledge on beauty. From catwalk collections of Paris, New York and Milan, to fashion and beauty shoots in St Lucia and Thailand, Ruby has done it all. She has also created looks for top photographers and influential designers, including John Galliano, Jasper Conran and Ghost. Her co-owned make-up range (Ruby & Millie) consists of almost 300 fantastic products.

Saibal Chatterjee

One of India's foremost critics of Hindi cinema, Saibal has been in the business for over two decades during which he has gained an insight into the changing style and attitudes influencing the worlds most dynamic film industry. Saibal was an editorial advisor of the Encyclopedia of Hindi Cinema and is a regular contributor to the Hindustan Times.

Saira Hussain

With over 12 years of experience in make-up, Saira has worked on mainstream music videos and television programmes for the likes of MTV and Top of the Pops. She is also often found backstage at fashion shows, beauty pageants and is regularly called upon for fashion shoots and for her bridal make-up expertise. Her company Kiss n Make-Up was formed in 1998 and since then she has trained and passed her skills onto her own team of hair and make-up artists as well as to students who are interested in a career in beauty.

Shavata

Eyebrow queen Shavata has worked in the beauty industry for over 19 years and is currently running her eyebrow studio at the Urban Retreat in London's prestigious department store, Harrods. Shavata has become a leader in her field and has forged a reputation as the authority on eyebrows. No one shapes and grooms brows in quite the same way as Shavata. She has a loyal clientele of top business women, models and well-known personalities.

Shenaz Shariff

Shenaz has trained in almost all areas of beauty. She specialises in hair removal treatments such as electrolysis and Epil-Pro, as well as skin disorders such as acne, pigmentation and scarring. Her salon also offers regular beauty treatments like body wraps, massages waxing, manicures, pedicures and facials. She also teaches and conducts seminars. Shenaz continues to research and test new treatments and products, working with the world's top doctors and scientists to determine what would work within the parameters of her clinic.

The Somatheeram Group

The Somatheeram Resort is one of Kerala's best-loved rejuvenation centres. It is packed with a host of Ayurvedic doctors who are arguably the best in the business and they still practice Ayurveda in its most natural form. The resort has its own medicine manufacturing unit run by a team of expert doctors. They also maintain a herbal garden with around 600 varieties of rare herbs, which are used for preparations of aromatic oils and exotic lotions for various treatments.

ACKNOWLEDGEMENTS

In putting this book together, I have had the privilege to work with some truly inspirational and talented people. A pick of the best international make-up artists and hair stylists have given me their time, patience and priceless trade secrets. Their stunning work is displayed in the pictures throughout the book. So a very big thank you to you all: Mickey Contractor, Cory Wallia, Kapil Bhalla, Mehera Khola, Pooja Arora, Nina Haider, Venus Ferrera, Adhuna Bhabhani-Akhtar and Dimple Sheikh from Yasmin @ Nailini & Yasmin.

The Ultimate Guide to Beauty is packed with handy insider tips, techniques and information. These 'insiders' are the authorities in their fields and their contributions and specialist advice has been invaluable - so thank you all for sharing your secrets.

I would like to thank my family and friends who have given me their time, encouragement, generosity and love...
First and foremost, a huge thanks to my husband Amar who read every chapter several times and has supported me all the way. My lovely mum for everything. My dad, brothers Shyam and Ram. My grandma Savita, Sonal Gosai, Jenna Mehmet, Jenny Pabila, Karishma Kotak, Supriya Prasad, Kerry Marco, Upen Patel, Ricky Patel, Naseeba Sacranie, Mary Rahman, Poonam Dev, Amish and Shum Gosai, Khuram Javaid, the girls at JWPR, Gulshan Grover, Tony Wellington, Amit Roy, Omar Qureshi, Mitika Chohan, the Eastern Eye team, Virchand Pindora, Shihab Salim and the rest of the gang at Asiana and to Samina Saeed and Sarwar Ahmed for giving me my first opportunity to work in the world of beauty.

I thank all the wonderful PR professionals who I constantly hound for products and quotes. Rana Danesh at Mac, Little Shilpa, Sheetal, Pradeep Mandhani, the B Blunt team, Sarang Kulkarni, Vishnu for the amazing ayurvedic drawings, Mangesh at Mukta Arts and Elite Model Management India.

A massive thanks to my photographer and friend Manoj Jadhav for capturing some beautiful images and for putting up with my demands, my top-class cover girl Ujjwala Raut and the gorgeous models Tapur Chatterjee, Indrani Dasgupta, Vanarose Heineman, Karishma Kotak, Sheetal Mallar, Vidisha Pavate, Dipannita Sharma, Tanya Vakil, Tinu Verghese and Elite`s Sucheta Sharma and Yasmin Ponnappa.

Special thanks to my editor Shoma Choudhury for her countless invaluable suggestions. A big thank you to Arvind Agarwal, Rajesh Khurana, Ashish Mago and Usha Raghuraman for all your hard work.

And finally, my deepest thanks go to the wonderful Aalok Wadhwa and Tahir Rafiq for your guidance, patience and believing in the book.

PICTURE CREDITS

COVER: Manoj Jadhav. Font design: Sarang Kulkarni. Make-up: Mickey Contractor. Hair: Adhuna Bhabhani-Akthar

INSIDE COVER: Manoj Jadhav. Make-up: Venus Ferrera. Hair: B-Blunt.

CONTENTS: Manoj Jadhav. Make-up: Venus Ferrrera

INTRODUCTION, page 5: Tony Wellington. Page 7: Manoj Jadhav. Page 10: Artist.

CHAPTER ONE, SKIN, page 13 & 14: Manoj Jadhav. Make-up: Cory Wallia and Pooja Arora. Page 16: Manoj Jadhav. Make-up: Pooja Arora. Page 20 & 22: Brian Heyes. Page 24: Mitika Chohan (illustration). Page 25 & 26: Manoj Jadhav. Make-up: Nina Haider. Page 28 & 29: Manoj Jadhav. Make-up: Venus Ferrera. Hair: B-Blunt.

CHAPTER TWO, GET TO KNOW YOUR FACE, page 33: Mausami Rege (illustration). Page 34: Manoj Jadhav. Make-up: Pooja Arora. Page 35: Mausami Rege (illustrations). Page 36: Manoj Jadhav. Make-up Mehera Khola.

CHAPTER THREE, TOOLS, page 39 - 41: Tony Wellington.

CHAPTER FOUR, FOUNDATION, page 45: Manoj Jadhav. Make-up: Mickey Contractor. Page 46: Tony Wellington. Page 50: Brian Heyes. Page 52: Manoj Jadhav. Page 53: Manoj Jadhav. Page 56: Brian Heyes.

CHAPTER FIVE, EYES, page 60: Manoj Jadhav: Make-up: Venus Ferrera. Accessories: Little Shilpa. Page 61: Space Nk. Page 64: Mausami Rege (illustrations). Page 65: Tony Wellington. Page 66: Manoj Jadhav. Page 67: Manoj Jadhave. Make-up Cory Wallia. Page 68: Mausami Rege (illustrations). Page 69 & 70: Manoj Jadhav. Make-up: Mehera Khola and Nina Haider. Page 72: Brian Heyes. Page 73: Manoj Jadhav: Make-up: Pooja Arora. Bikini: Malini Ramani. Page 75: Manoj Jadhav. Make-up: Kapil Bhalla. Page 77: Manoj Jadhav. Make-up: Mickey Contractor. Page 78: Mausami Rege (illustrations). Page 80: Brian Heyes. Page 81: L'Officiel India. Photography by Farrokh Chothia. Styling Anaita Shroff-Adjania. Make-up: Kapil Bhalla. Page 82: Tony Wellington.

CHAPTER SIX, CHEEKS, page 86: Manoj Jadhav. Make-up: Pooja Arora. Page 87: Brian Heyes. Page 88: Mausami Rege (illustrations). Page 90: Manoj Jadhave: Make-up: Venus Ferrera.

CHAPTER SEVEN, LIPS, page 93 & 94: Manoj Jadhav. Make-up: Corey Wallia. Page 95: Brian Heyes. Page 97 & 98: Mausami Rege (illustrations). Page 100: Manoj Jadhav. Make-up; Cory Wallia. Mask: Basia Zarzycka.

CHAPTER EIGHT, HANDS & FEET, page 104: Manoj Jadhav. Page 106: Brian Heyes. Page 107: Manoj Jadhav.

CHAPTER NINE, HAIR, page 111: Manoj Jadhav. Make-up: Cory Wallia. Necklace: Amrapali. Page 116: Manoj Jadhav. Make-up: Mehera Khola. Page 118 & 120: Brian Heyes. Page 122: Manoj Jadhav. Make-up: Nina Haider. Flower: Bascia Zarzycka. Bikini: Vishal Kapoor.

CHAPER TEN, UNWANTED HAIR, page 125: Manoj Jadhav. Make-up: Mehera Khola. Jewellery: Amrapali. Page 128: Manoj Jadhav. Make-up: Mehera Khola. Necklace: Amrapali. Page 130: Brian Heyes.

CHAPTER ELEVEN, BRIDAL BEAUTY, page 133 & 134: Tony Wellington. Page 135: Manoj Jadhav. Make-up: Mickey Contractor. Outfit: Tarun Tahiliani. Page 137: Manoj Jadhav. Make-up: Cory Wallia. Outfit: AD Singh. Necklace: Amrapali. Page 140: Manoj Jadhav. Make-up: Venus Ferrera: Hair: B-Blunt. Hair piece: Little Shilpa. Page 141 & 142: Bridal Asia.

CHAPTER TWELVE, HENNA, page 145: Ash Kumar (illustration). Page 148: Brian Heyes.

CHAPTER THIRTEEN, BOLLYWOOD BEAUTY, page 152-158: National Film Archives of India. Page 159: Mukta Arts. Page 160: Mukta Arts.

CHAPTER FOURTEEN, CATWALK SECRETS, page 163-168: Pradeep Mandhani. Tony Wellington (stills).

CHAPTER FIFTEEN, BODY & MIND, page 172 & 173 Vishnu (illustrations). Page 174, 175 & 177: Brian Heyes. Page 178: Manoj Jadhav. Page 179: Manoj Jadhav. Make-up: Venus Ferrera. Hair: B-Blunt. Page 181: Brian Heyes.

INSIDE BACK COVER: Manoj Jadhav. Make-up: Kapil Bhalla.

BACK COVER: Brian Heyes.

GLOSSARY

ALOE VERA
Aloe vera is a short-stemmed plant growing and is native to North Africa. The sap from the aloe vera plant is commonly used to treat various skin conditions such as cuts, burns and eczema. It can help to ease pain and reduce inflammation

ANDROGEN
A steroid hormone, such as testosterone or androsterone, that controls the development and maintenance of masculine characteristics.

CONDITIONING AGENT
An ingredient that usually acts by attracting and holding moisture in the skin or hair.

DÈCOLLETAGE
Word used to describe the area between the neck and shoulders on a female body.

EMOLLIENT
An agent that softens or soothes the skin.

HYPERPIGMENTATION
Hyperpigmentation is a common condition in which patches of skin become darker in color than the normal surrounding area.

HYPOALLERGENIC
A term used to describe cosmetics that cause or are claimed to cause fewer allergic reactions.

MELANIN
Melanin is a substance that gives the skin its natural color. Those with darker skin have higher amounts of melanin.

ORANGE STICK
A thin stick, pointed at one end and typically made of orange wood, used for manicuring the fingernails

PATCH TEST
A method used to determine if a specific product (cosmetic, skincare or hair product) causes an inflammation or allergy.

PORES
A pore is the tiny opening of the hair follicle onto the surface of the skin. They provide a way for the oil glands underneath to lubricate and protect the skin's surface.

SEBUM
Sebum is made up of fat and the debris of dead fat-producing cells. Sebum can cause oily skin or greasy feeling hair.

SEBACEOUS GLANDS
The role of the sebaceous glands is to secrete oil (sebum). This oil helps to keep the skin lubricated.

T-ZONE
The T-zone is the part of the face consisting of the forehead, nose and the area around the mouth. It is so named because it is shaped like the letter 'T'.

UV RAYS
Ultraviolet (UV) rays are invisible rays emitted by the sun. The main ultraviolet rays that reach the earth are UVA, UVB and UVC. UVA rays have the ability to reach deep into the skin to break down collagen. UVB rays cause sunburn and in worst cases skin cancer.

INDEX